UNIVERSITY OF KNOWLEDGE

GLENN FRANK, B.A., M.A., Litt.D., L.H.D., LL.D., *Editor-in-Chief*

PRINTED AND BOUND IN THE UNITED STATES
OF AMERICA BY THE CUNEO PRESS, INC.

Every Branch of Knowledge Man Possesses May Be Applied To Some Good Purpose

INDIAN SNOW LEOPARD

UNIVERSITY OF KNOWLEDGE

GLENN FRANK, EDITOR-IN-CHIEF

TRAILING ANIMALS
AROUND
THE WORLD

EDITED BY

CHARLES H. SEEVERS, PH. D.,

Author, Educator, and
Lecturer in Zoölogy

UNIVERSITY OF KNOWLEDGE, INCORPORATED

CHICAGO

INTRODUCTION

This is a volume that tells of animals, wild and tame, commonplace and strange, and of birds, reptiles, and insects, their habits and their habitats.

The Greek philosopher summed up what seemed to him the way to wisdom in the counsel Know Thyself. This series of volumes has been built around the conviction that the way to wisdom is to know both yourself and your world. Since animals are a part of your world it is important that you know them.

Our ancestors on the frontiers they successively conquered knew a wide variety of animals—the bear, the fox, the wolf, the deer, the buffalo, and the oxen that pulled their covered wagons westward. As time and civilization marched on, this animal variety was diluted. Many of us went through boyhoods without knowing more than dogs and cats and horses and cows and sheep and goats, save as the seasonal circus widened our eyes with wonder at strange and exotic animals and birds and reptiles.

This volume attempts to widen our wonder and deepen our knowledge as the circus never did. Our interest in animals is wider and deeper as adults than when as children we trudged with high hearts to the circus.

We are hunters lured by the excitement of the chase.

We are naturalists bent upon discovery and description.

We are animal lovers extracting pleasure from the breeding, owning, and training of domestic animals.

We are travelers intent upon observing the animal world at home on plains, in swamps, in jungles, and in the high reaches of mountains.

We are scientists pursuing the elusive facts of physiology,

anatomy, bio-chemistry, bacteriology, and varied matters of structure and function important to the breath and being of our own lives by patient and painstaking study of animals.

We are anti-vivisectionists protesting the use of animals as living laboratories in medical research.

We are conservationists determined that neither the hunter nor the researcher nor the lax legislator shall denude the land of a rich and varied animal life.

None of us is all these. All of us are one or more of these. Whatever our point of contact and interest with the animal world, it is important to widen our knowledge of it.

One does not need to be a Viscount Grey or a Theodore Roosevelt, those two amazing amateurs in natural history, to thrill to the sight of a flaming cardinal or find joy in the lilting song of a lark. This book is designed to give its readers a start towards achieving the knowledge of animals and birds and insects and reptiles that invested the lives of the Greys and the Roosevelts with so much color and interest.

This is not a text-book of natural history. It has sought to escape the sober sterility of a long and detailed catalogue of species. It is rather a travel book of the animal world. Its authors, with their curiosity and their cameras, scour the world and bring back to us a succinct story and visual reproduction of the most interesting and most important of the varied species of animals, birds, reptiles, and insects. The table of contents gives a quick sense of the scope and colorful interest of their tours.

Here is an interest that a fully rounded life cannot afford to miss. Neither you nor I may ever be able to look in on Africa, India, Australia, the South Pacific Islands, China, Northern Eurasia, the Arctic, Canada, Mexico, Central and South America, and all the rest, to say nothing of the varied regions of the United States. But we can become "tasters" of the joys of the naturalist by reading this book and then following its myriad clues into still other books, wider in their scope or more comprehensive in their details.

All in all, I have enjoyed injecting this volume into this series quite as much as I have enjoyed the determination of any volume in the series, just because my own life has been strangely deficient in knowledge of the animal world. Already the manuscript of this volume has sent me scurrying to bookstores to find out more about this or that animal or group of animals the authors of this volume have brought to capture my interest.

GLENN FRANK, *Editor-in-chief.*

PREFACE

Man's curiosity regarding himself is almost equaled by his curiosity about all other forms of life that inhabit the earth with him. He has set apart hundreds of acres of wild land in order to perpetuate certain species which have been endangered by extinction. He has collected groups of them from the wide-spread corners of the earth, and placed them in zoölogical gardens so that he may view the strange denizens of strange lands. He has sent out expeditions to these strange lands to gather living specimens to exhibit. His interest in these animals, birds, fish, and reptiles is best demonstrated by the popularity of the wild-animal displays in circuses which are perpetual delights both to young and old.

Coincidentally with this curiosity there has grown up a mass of ridiculous misinformation, myths, and folklore regarding the habits of these creatures. Because many of them exhibit certain "human" qualities, the ignorant have come to believe that some animals are reincarnations of human beings. Even the reverse is thought to be true of various people. The French *loup-garou,* for instance, is supposed to be an evil person who can turn himself into a wolf. The vampire bat, in certain sections, is thought to be a blood-sucking human being who can change himself at will. The ancient Egyptians deified many animals and made sacrifices to them. Members of a religious sect in the South Sea Islands worship the snake, and have erected a temple to it. In India, many animals have been made sacrosanct and any people who molest them are subject to death.

One of the strangest myths concerns the supposed burial grounds of the African elephants. Rumor had it that there was a certain spot deep in the jungle wilds to which sick elephants repaired when they knew they were dying. Dozens of expeditions braved the dangers of the jungles attempting to uncover this burial ground. They reasoned that thousands of elephants must have died there and left thousands of tons of valuable ivory. To date, in spite of the many expeditions, no such "elephant grave-yard" has been found.

Another tenacious, erroneous belief is that the ostrich hides its head in the sand when trouble is near. Nothing more ridiculous can be thought of regarding this bird, which is keen-sighted and speedy enough to outdistance even a horse. The ostrich, instead of being one of the oldest of living birds, would have been extinct hundreds of years ago had it been guilty of such inane tactics.

Snakes have come in for their share of myths and tall tales. The hoop snake, which is supposed to be able to shape itself into a circle and roll out of danger, is the classic. The milk snake is said to be fond of cow's milk, and the glass snake is supposed to be so brittle that, when an enemy approaches, it can splinter itself to pieces and then recompose itself again. Of course, these stories are additional examples of wild imaginings. Perhaps the most fallacious story about the snake is that it is able to hypnotize its victims before striking out with its poisonous fangs.

More than two thousand years ago Aristotle wrote that certain birds—vultures, herons and various songbirds—migrated across the Mediterranean Sea, between Africa and southern Europe, in the spring and fall. Naturalists scoffed at him at the time and called him insane. Yet, only as recently as Washington's time, New Englanders thought that with the approach of winter, birds buried themselves deep in bogs and swamps, transformed into frogs, lizards, and turtles. When spring returned they reverted to the chrysalis stage again and emerged as birds.

The effect of these folk-tales regarding animals is more far-reaching than is apparent. Many an innocent person has been put to death because he was suspected of being a *loup garou* or a vampire. A number of species of birds and animals have been almost eradicated because they were thought to feed on grain or fowl. An examination of the crops of many birds suspected of eating grain proved that instead they ate certain insects which were harmful to growing things. Such birds, of course, were thus helpful instead of harmful.

The purpose of this book is first to be entertaining. Scientific names and data have been cut down to a minimum. Descriptions have been written vividly, without the deadly monotony apparent in many treatises on natural history. But, it is hoped that this book, while being entertaining may serve in adding to the reader's knowledge of birds and beasts. Naturally, the physical limitations prohibit a comprehensive treatment of every animal and bird known to man, but a sincere attempt has been made to describe as many of the interesting fauna as is possible. If the reader is able to garner information about those chosen, he will have enriched himself greatly and he will have furnished himself with knowledge which should increase his understanding of the world in which he lives and the living things that inhabit it with him.

The assistance of the following persons in writing this volume is gratefully acknowledged: Mr. Lewis Herman, Captain G. E. Nightingale, Mrs. Bonnie Esterquest, Mr. Donald Morris, Mr. John D. Weidenfeller, Miss Anna Mae Daly, and Mr. Martin J. Engberg.

CHARLES H. SEEVERS

Chicago
January 24, 1938

ACKNOWLEDGMENT

The fascinating animal life of the jungles of Africa, India, and South America; of the vast steppes of Siberia and the wide plains of North America; of the frozen regions of the Arctic and the warm waters of tropical seas, is pictured in this volume. The mighty elephant, the enormous whale, the lizard, the termite, the bird of paradise, and the household pet are all found in this book, which gives a complete picture of the animals, reptiles, and birds of every continent and clime.

We wish to express our appreciation for the personal assistance of Captain George Elliott-Nightingale, and also for the co-operation of the following persons and institutions:

National Parks of Canada
Chicago Park District, Lincoln Park Zoölogical
    Gardens
New York Zoölogical Society
American Museum of Natural History
United States Department of Agriculture, Biological
    Survey
United States Department of the Interior
Australian Railways
Canadian National Railways
South African Railways
Mason Warner Company
Sears Roebuck Company
Field Museum of Natural History, Chicago
Hudson's Bay Company
Doctor Frank P. Thompson

J. BRADFORD PENGELLY,
Picture Editor

TABLE OF CONTENTS

AFRICAN MALE LION
(After a painting by Rosa Bonheur.)

[XVI]

EXPLORING THE HEART OF AFRICA

LIVINGSTONE'S IMMORTAL WORK

AFRICA, teeming with weird forms of life, is a fascinating continent. Its very name brings to mind a world of mystery where strange peoples struggle for existence with fierce animals and dark jungles.

Africa is a land of amusing and tragic surprises, a realm of sharp contrasts, amazing contradictions, stark realities. Intense dry heat, insufferable humidity, deep snows, and even sub-zero cold may be experienced all in one day in certain equatorial regions. In those same areas, beautiful with luxuriant vegetation, are deadly diseases borne by insects.

On the fringes of this vast continent, and also in strategic areas in the hinterland, live Africa's six million white people. Elsewhere, on the plains and in the jungles, are one hundred twenty-three million Negroes and Negroids, and about twenty-five million Berbers, Arabs, Egyptians, and Galas. The composition and characteristics of the black-skinned millions vary widely. Some are nomadic and warlike, while others are semi-civilized, peaceful, and interested largely in primitive agriculture.

In many and varied ways Africa is still the "dark continent." In fact, what little we know of it has been gathered within the past one hundred years. Light was first shed on "darkest Africa" by the immortal Dr. David Livingstone. This dean of all medical missionaries arrived at Algoa Bay in Southeastern Africa, in the

DR. DAVID LIVINGSTONE

SIR HENRY M. STANLEY, NOTED EXPLORER WHO FOUND DR. LIVINGSTONE

year 1841. Humbly he bent to his work of the practical application. of Christianity and medicine to savage peoples, never dreaming that the day would come when he, and he alone, would be the center of world-wide attention; never dreaming, moreover, that in attracting the world's attention he would be opening the door to an unknown continent five times larger in area than the United States.

Once inside Africa's portals, this great but simple man opened other doors: those leading into the mysterious hinterland. After several years of substantial and commendable work in Bechuanaland, he crossed the Kalahari Desert and arrived at Lake Ngami in 1849. Two years later, the very nature of his work having by now transformed him into an explorer, Dr. Livingstone discovered the Zambesi River. Four years later, in 1855, he continued his exploration of the Zambesi, discovering the glorious and magnificent Victoria Falls. During the two years that followed he pushed on through Portuguese East Africa, to Quilimane on the coast. After a short time here, in the capacity of British consul, he was given command of an official exploration party which was to carry on a wider and more comprehensive exploration of the Zambesi country. Eight years passed during which little was heard of the missionary-explorer. The few letters and reports that did get to England, however, were veritable treasure-chests of hitherto unknown facts and truths concerning the darkest places of a continent clothed in mystery. In 1865 he returned to England and was received as a long-lost son. It was then that Dr. David Livingstone turned to the writing of the first dependable books about the "dark continent," books filled with the reports of Christian endeavor in a savage country, narratives seasoned with the thrill of travel, adventure, and incomparable discoveries.

The Royal Geographic Society in 1866 gave Livingstone the command of an expedition that was to search for the source of the Nile. Five years went by, and there were frequent reports that the great Dr. Livingstone was lost in the African jungles. During 1871, these reports were becoming increasingly frequent, and the whole civilized world grew anxious. People in all walks of life were asking, "Where is Livingstone?"

Each day interest in this missionary-explorer's fate grew more and more intense. Each day an anxious world asked if Dr. David Livingstone was alive or dead. Prince and pauper alike wondered if the cannibals had perpetrated some of their ghastly work; and they wondered, too, if the great missionary might not have perished in the frightful maw of a python, or under the claws of ferocious beasts. And then, as the whole world waited breathlessly for some new development, an American publisher, James Gordon Bennett, called in his most resourceful and most talented writer, a young man known to the world later as Henry M. Stanley. When Stanley appeared, James Gordon Bennett said but two words: "Find Livingstone." During the months that followed, those two words were indelibly written on Stanley's heart and soul. Over the trackless wastes of ocean and desert, and along the dangerous jungle trails, the command echoed and re-echoed: "Find Livingstone!" Then came the happy day when the enterprising Henry M. Stanley, pushing his way through the Tanganyika country, learned that a bewildered and very ill white man was being cared for by natives at the tiny settlement of

Ujiji, on the eastern shores of Lake Tanganyika. Driving his porters relentlessly, Stanley made all possible speed for Ujiji. There his quest ended with the famous greeting, "Mr. Livingstone, I presume."

In spite of his advanced age and evident infirmity, David Livingstone flatly refused to return to England with Stanley. Without realizing it, the courageous explorer was nearing the end of life's trail. Suffering and hardship were beginning to take their toll, and two years later he passed away in the tiny jungle village of Ilala which nestles on the banks of the Lulimala. Grief-stricken natives carried his remains several hundreds of miles to the coast for shipment to England where they now rest in the peaceful silence of Westminster Abbey.

Today, David Livingstone's letters, reports, and fascinating books contain what has proved to be the first reliable and dependable information about the "dark continent," as Livingstone called it. He gave us much of value, and in the giving he opened the first door that has since permitted many to enter his beloved Africa. And yet, in spite of the abundance of information at hand, eminent explorers and scientists are agreed that we have barely scratched the surface of things African. Scientists are searching ceaselessly for more knowledge about African life.

On the east coast, at a point about four degrees below the equator, is the seaport of Mombasa. Centuries before the Christian Era, Arabian traders wandered up and down this bit of coast trading in gold, ivory, and slaves. Mombasa was great, important, and rich, a crossroads of the East. Nor has time detracted anything from Mombasa's importance, for even in these days it remains the favorite "jumping off" place for explorers and scientists.

THE LION, KING OF THE PLAINS AND LOWLANDS

Leaving Mombasa on the Uganda Railway, one quickly comes to a veritable naturalists' paradise. One hundred miles up country is the heart of the famous Tsavo region which is the locale of Colonel J. H. Patterson's book, *The Man-Eaters of Tsavo*. Very little was known of this particular area until 1898 when the

Courtesy Chicago Park District

AFRICAN MALE LION, JUST A LITTLE BORED AND READY FOR SLEEP

Courtesy Chicago Park District

YOUNG AFRICAN LIONESS IN PENSIVE MOOD

steel of the British-built Uganda Railway began to push through it. The railroad builders had unfortunate experiences with man-eating lions, which were numerous in the Tsavo country.

The most dangerous big game in Africa include the lion, leopard, rhinoceros, elephant, and buffalo. Naturally, each has its own peculiarities, its own type of cunning, and its own brand of ferocity. On the question of which one of the above is the most dangerous, there is some disagreement among those qualified to voice opinions. In its own way, the ponderous rogue elephant can be just as dangerous and ferocious as the hungry lion. It should be mentioned, of course, that there are other animals dangerous to the unarmed and unsuspecting human abroad in the jungle and on the plain, but most of these are not particularly dangerous from the viewpoint of the hunter who understands them.

It is generally conceded, however, that although the lion might not be the king of beasts, he is at least the king of the African

Courtesy South African Railways

AFRICAN MALE LION RESTING AFTER A BIG FEED

plains and swampy lowlands. Generally speaking, he is just a great big cat, the largest species of the feline family. He is entirely flesh-eating, and is remarkably well equipped with sharp claws and much sharper fangs so that he can get the meat he must have. His sight is as keen by night as by day, and his sensitive whiskers guide him as he prowls through the darkness under the tangled vegetation blanketing the forest floor. This does not mean that he makes his home in the depths of the forests. Instead, he prefers rocky, broken country that is half bushland and half plain and meadow.

The lion, with its tawny, short-haired skin, blends amazingly well with the flora of the meadows and open places. So effective is this blending that many a man has walked to within yards of a sleeping lion before actually seeing the animal. Especially is this blending in favor of the lioness which does not grow the darker-haired mane that often reveals the location of a male lion at rest.

Among the lion's favorite sources of food are the zebra, giraffe, antelope, and buffalo. Although lions prefer freshly killed meat, they will feed upon any rotting carcasses available, or will visit a white man's camp or a jungle village and help themselves to a human being or two if the risks are not too great. Generally speaking, man-eating lions are usually aged, crippled, or otherwise incapable of holding their own in the strenuous attack necessary to bring down such game as one of the larger and heavier antelopes like the eland, which often attains a weight of fifteen hundred pounds. However, young lions have been known to be man-eaters. At any rate, it is generally agreed that the lion does not eat human flesh except when compulsion leaves no other choice.

Needless to say, the speed, strength, and agility of the lion are phenomenal. Stalking its prey, moving relentlessly along the trail with the quiet and stealth of a house cat crossing a carpeted parlor, a three-hundred-pound lion will quickly bring down an animal weighing a thousand pounds or more. The lion's killing technique is an example of "raw" nature. After getting into position by stalking his prey, perhaps a zebra, a short swift run is followed by an astonishingly elastic bound which lands the lion on the zebra's back. Instantly his sharp front claws sink deeply into the neck of the panic-stricken zebra, while the equally sharp and penetrating hind claws sink into rump or flank. Thus anchored, and with the animal in full gallop or cavorting wildly, the lion sinks his four long sharp fangs deep into the victim's neck. Again and again, with startling rapidity, those murderous fangs sink in to the very gums until the prey's backbone gives way and the spinal cord is severed. Then, before the animal is dead, the great cat begins tearing and rending the skin and flesh. Hours later, sated with fresh blood and meat, his distended stomach showing the effect of gluttonous gorging, he retires to some quiet, shady spot where he will sleep and rest until hunger again drives him forth to another kill. Meanwhile, as he sleeps and takes life easy, vultures, hyenas, jackals, wild dogs, and other smaller carnivora clean up what remains of the kill.

Although the hungry lion might bring down a fleet-footed zebra after the manner described above, he follows a somewhat different method when bringing down the smaller antelopes. Springing at the victim's head, he will sink his front claws into head and neck. Thus holding the head in fierce grasp, he shifts his position until he can sink those terrifying fangs in the neck, and he will keep this up until he has bitten through backbone and spinal cord and the animal is done for. Sometimes, too, a mere swing or blow from a front leg or paw will bring the prey down with a broken neck. Then, with all opposition out of the way, the lion, with fang and claw rips open the belly and goes after such tidbits as the heart, liver, and kidneys.

Although he is undoubtedly courageous, most of the lion's depredations are made against smaller game, all of which gives rise to the opinion of some African explorers that the lion, instead of being a king among beasts, is really a bully, attacking those animals smaller and far less muscular than himself.

A full-grown male might measure ten or eleven feet from nose to the tip of his tufted tail, and stand between three and four feet high at the shoulders. Weight varies, of course, according to the animal's general condition, but a matured male with the above proportions would probably weigh five hundred pounds. The females are generally a little lighter in weight and shorter in length and height. The lions of Algeria, Somaliland, and else-where in Africa resemble the previously described species so close-ly that it is unnecessary to treat them separately. Naturally their habits change according to regions, and also according to available food supplies.

Generally, the female gives birth to two, three, or perhaps four cubs once a year. She guards them closely, too, for the male is fond of lion-cubs for breakfast.

THE LEOPARD

One of the craftiest of ferocious beasts, the leopard is more dangerous even than the lion or tiger. As with the tiger, its spots serve as a protective coloring. The background of the fur is almost always a reddish-yellow, although some run from white to black. Superimposed more or less uniformly over this back-

Courtesy Chicago Park District

"BILLIE," AN AFRICAN LEOPARD TEN YEARS OLD
It takes eight pounds of fresh beef every day to keep him satisfied and in good health.

ground are a number of black spots which give the fur its gorgeous appearance. In overall length, the leopard averages about seven feet, three feet of which are taken up with a spotted tail. Like cats and unlike lions and tigers, the leopard climbs trees quite easily and stalks its unwary prey from trees, leaping with sinuous agility from limb to limb. When it pounces murderously, it takes hold of the animal's neck with its powerful fangs and breaks it. Then it drags the carcass away for feeding. When surfeited with food, the leopard hides what is left of the carcass in a branch cleft and returns to it later on, regardless of its state of putrefaction. It is for this reason that the bite of a leopard is so dangerous to mankind, not because of the wound itself but because of the certain infection that sets in. It will and has attacked man, but its usual diet is monkeys, pigs, antelopes, birds, and reptiles. At the age of three, when it is full grown, the leopard may become a man-eater and it is then that he is most dangerous, especially when he has not been able to catch food animals. When wounded, instead of slinking into the brush, it turns on its tormentor and continues to attack, slashing with its fangs and ripping away flesh with its powerful hind legs that are barbarously armed with long curving claws.

SMALLER FLESH-EATERS

The hyena is the chief of the four-footed scavengers that roam the plains and jungles. He will eat just about any kind of the most putrid animal matter, and thus, in his way, performs a valuable service in disposing of carrion. The largest of the three species of African hyenas is known as the spotted hyena. As his name implies, his yellow-brown fur is spotted with black-brown blotches. Mature and in good condition, he might measure six feet from the nose to the tip of the tail. His front legs are longer than the hind ones, which gives him the appearance of holding his head rather high. He is more stoutly built and more muscular and aggressive than the striped hyena of North Africa, Asia, or India, or the still smaller brown striped species found in the south of Africa. Although a member of the dog family, the hyena is noted more for his cowardice than his courage. Equipped

Courtesy New York Zoological Society

SPOTTED HYENA OF AFRICA
Largest member of the hyena family.

with powerful, muscular jaws and strong sharp teeth, he has been known to carry off children. He seldom kills his own food, but waits to feed upon the remains of the lion's freshest kill. Now and then, however, there are savage and courageous hyenas that not only attack human beings but also attack and kill donkeys, small zebras, and antelopes. Like a smart fox terrier worrying a rat, the hyena will harry and harass his quarry to exhaustion. Then, with lightning speed he attacks the victim's belly with his strong, sharp fangs, and begins to eat the entrails while the prey is still alive. Near the settlements, hyenas cause damage among unsuspecting, defenseless farm cattle.

The African jackal is in many respects similar to the hyenas. Like them, he is a member of the dog family. Individually sly, furtive, and somewhat cowardly, jackals usually hunt in packs;

this, of course, enables them to bring down ordinary farm cattle and some of the antelopes. Like hyenas, they are nocturnal, and when "on the run" they raid the pig pens and poultry houses of the settlements, or prowl through the villages eating all the offal and garbage within sight and smell, thus doing beneficial sanitary work where it is most needed. There are various regional species, none of which is very large. A mature specimen will measure from twenty-five to thirty inches from nose to tail-tip, stand about fifteen inches high at the shoulder, and weigh from twenty to twenty-five pounds after a hearty meal. The Indian and Asiatic species resemble the African species too closely to call for special mention.

GIRAFFES

The Kapiti region is a mixture of bush country and plains, and is ideal as the home of the giraffe which blends well with its environment. There are nine or ten varieties of giraffes, all members of either the southern or northern species. The latter are found down the Nile and in Abyssinia, while the former range from the Sudan through East Central Africa and farther south. These animals have a weird appearance with their long, stilt-like legs, tapered necks, and small heads. Between the ears are skin-covered projections that look like horns. However, they are merely protruding growths of certain bones in the skull, and occur in both sexes. In the forest regions of Ituri, there are giraffes which have four or even five well-developed "horns," while those in the Kapiti area have but two or three.

The giraffe is a harmless and inoffensive creature, but he can do some very effective kicking with his cloven hoofs, even to giving a large lion a good trouncing. On the run, they can travel almost thirty miles per hour, presenting a ludicrous and very amusing picture as they keep their tapering neck as stiff as possible, while they go into a loping bouncing gallop. Like most mammals, the giraffe has only seven vertebrae in its neck, despite the length of that member. Giraffes, being herbivorous, prefer open forested country. Moreover, owing to the fact that they can take in so much moisture with their food, they resemble the camel in being able to go for many days without quenching their thirst.

Courtesy South African Railways

THE AFRICAN GIRAFFE
They sometimes provide a much relished meal for the lion family.

Perhaps the most interesting feature connected with their tree-top feeding and browsing concerns their long and very flexible tongue. This organ in the mature animal will measure from sixteen to eighteen inches in length and is a great aid in reaching out to obtain luscious morsels high up on a branch. In captivity, however, the giraffe's diet consists largely of hay and certain vegetables, especially carrots. Lacking vocal cords, the giraffe is a silent animal, so he cannot show his desire or appreciation for food by grunts, or noise of any kind. About the only noise he can make is an ordinary snort. Some idea of their value can be obtained from the price range in Nairobi, famous shipping point for African animals. In Nairobi the price ranges from two to three hundred dollars, sometimes more for a good specimen, but

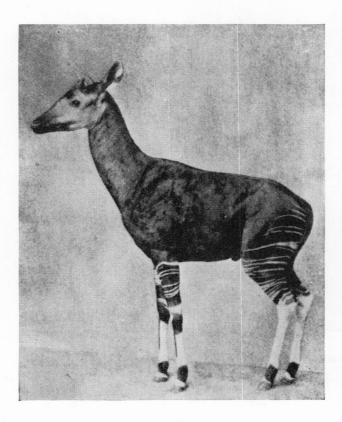

THE OKAPI, ONLY LIVING RELATIVE OF THE GIRAFFE

Discovered by Sir Harry Johnson in 1900; still quite rare.

Courtesy Field Museum of Natural History

by the time the animal reaches some far-off zoo he is worth many times that amount.

A peculiar species of giraffe was discovered in 1899 near the jungle settlement of Mbeni when an explorer found the natives working over some strangely marked hides, which aroused the interest of a naturalist who later visited the Mbeni region and identified this animal as a species of giraffe. There was some difficulty in ascertaining the native name for this newly discovered animal. In one place the natives called it the "kwapi," while a mile or two away other natives called it the "okwapi." Within recent years, however, the white man has spoken of this peculiar giraffe as the *okapi*. When full-grown it attains a shoulder height of about five feet, while the body may be somewhat shorter. The okapi is purplish in color, with the sides of the face a combination of dark-brown and purple. The limbs are barred with black and white, while some specimens have white "stockings" on the lower part of the hind legs. The ears are quite large, and the very short "horns," unlike those of the true giraffe, protrude through the skin. In the true giraffes both sexes have these skin-covered bone "horns," while in the okapi family the male alone is horned. Unlike the true giraffe, the okapi spends most of its life in the deep jungles and little-known forests where it feeds on leaves, shrubbery, and other plant life. Living in the densest jungles it is very difficult to locate, and therefore is quite a rarity.

THE SWIFT-FOOTED ANTELOPES

Africa has more than a hundred species of antelopes widely scattered through the continent. In the Kapiti country, where the giraffe is so prominent, is the waterbuck, which belongs to the antelope family. The particular species is identified by the elliptical "brand" or circle of white on each rump. Feeding largely on aquatic plants, waterbucks naturally frequent the reedy and swampy places by the rivers and lakes, usually traveling in small herds led by a large battle-scarred old buck. Like the giraffe, the waterbuck occasionally furnishes a meal for the lion.

Courtesy A. J. Klein of the Kenya Association

AFRICAN WILDEBEESTS AT THE WATERHOLE

Courtesy Dr. Frank P. Thompson, Chicago

AFRICAN WATERBUCK, MEMBER OF
THE ANTELOPE FAMILY

Another antelope, the hartebeest, is brownish-bay in color. Both sexes have lyrate, corrugated horns that bend forward slightly, and then turn abruptly backward. The hair along the back is of a purplish hue. Especially noticeable are the stockily built forequarters, the high withers, and the very narrow and somewhat drooping hindquarters. In spite of this somewhat clumsy build, however, the hartebeest is a tough customer, and at times hard to kill even with bullets.

The impala is a swift-footed antelope about the size of fallow deer. It feeds in low swampy places and, when suddenly frightened, seems to jump straight upward for three or four feet. Touching the ground again, it leaps away on another twisting jump, covering the ground with amazing speed which enables it to make a quick escape from natural enemies, especially the lion.

The eland, largest of the African antelopes, makes its home in the Kijabe country. The full-grown bulls may be six feet in height at the shoulder, and some specimens have attained a weight of over fifteen hundred pounds. Their horns, common to both species, are spiraled and grow straight up with considerable spreading. The short, smooth hair is usually bright fawn in color, but the bulls lose so much hair in old age that the blue tint of the skin shows through. The northern species is identified by the thin, white vertical lines from two to four inches apart that course from back to belly. The meat of this animal, exceptionally tasty and nourishing, is favored by explorers and big-game hunters. Elands graze like domestic cattle, and when one gazes at them from a distance, the cows can be distinguished by their reddish-brown color.

The elands were practically exterminated by 1890, and those of Central Africa were nearly swept away by rinderpest a few years later. Very few are left at present, even in the remote districts. However, a second and larger species, or subspecies, still exists in large numbers in Western and Equatorial Africa. Along the Semliki frontier one may find an antelope with a strange name, the shy and timid *dik dik*. Smallest of African antelopes, the mature dik dik weighs less than ten pounds. His shoulder height is between twelve and fourteen inches, and his body-length about twenty. His full-grown, well-developed spike horns are at least

SPLENDID SPECIMEN OF THE
BULL ELAND
This species was first drawn to public notice
by the illustrious Dr. Livingstone.

Courtesy Dr. Frank P. Thompson, Chicago

three inches in length, and between the horns is a tuft of grey-brown hair. His flesh is tasty, and two hungry explorers could easily eat a dik dik for breakfast. Other species of the dik dik are found in West Africa and also in the forested regions of Abyssinia. Small as he is, the dik dik is not the smallest antelope in the animal kingdom. The pygmy musk antelope, native to Guinea, is much smaller. When full-grown, this little antelope reaches about eight inches in height and about fifteen inches in length. Not much larger than a good-sized rabbit, two of them could be eaten at one sitting by a hungry explorer.

Courtesy Field Museum of Natural History

ABYSSINIAN DIK DIK—SMALL MEMBERS OF THE ANTELOPE FAMILY

Going into the lower and less hilly and mountainous districts and out onto the small plains one sees Dorcas', Grant's, and Speke's gazelles. Gazelle is a general term applied to about twenty species of African antelopes. They are herbivorous, and some species, like the camel, are reputed to be able to go for extended periods without quenching their thirst. In addition to these gazelles, we also see the white and the beisa oryx, other species of antelopes.

Gazelles are to be found in a number of places, particularly in the North African deserts, the Arabian deserts, Asia Minor, and central Asia. Perhaps the most beautiful of them all is Grant's gazelle, found in eastern Africa, around the Lake Rudolph region and southward to Ugogo. The male of this species is about thirty-four inches in height at its shoulders. Short-haired, its fur is of a fawn color on the back shading into pure white around its hindquarters and its belly. A ring of red edged with white extends from its nose to the horns. Its short tail is tipped with a black tuft while the upper portion is white. Its long horns are beautifully formed, running vertically from its head for about

Courtesy Chicago Park District

THE AFRICAN ORYX

Black Star photo by William Fox

ONE OF AFRICA'S GAZELLES

six inches and then curving out gracefully and horizontally in streamline fashion, sometimes growing to lengths of thirty inches in the male. Most outstanding of its features are its large, sultry, and limpid eyes which Persian poets have compared with the eyes of a woman.

Like its horns, the gazelle's limbs and body are streamlined so that in flight it is both speedy and graceful as it goes skimming over the plains, seeming almost never to touch the ground with its sharp-pointed hoofs. Swifter than the greyhound, the gazelle can show its hoofs even to the speedy lion and leopard, which can catch it only by cunning. The Arabs are forced to use trained falcons which harass the animal and impede its flight until their dogs can draw up for the kill. Never living in the jungles or mountains, it can be found only on the plains in both small and large herds, running with zebras and hartebeests.

Because of its odd and short name, most people know of the *gnu* only because it haunts the squares of crossword puzzles. Its habitat is in the Karoo north of Cape Colony while another species is to be found from Bechuanaland to British East Africa. The Dutch Boers called the gnu the "wildebeest" because of its almost mad habits and its strange appearance. It has the ponderous head of a buffalo, the horns of a bull, which both sexes carry,

Courtesy South African Railways

HERD OF WILDEBEESTS IN THE KRUGER NATIONAL PARK, SOUTH AFRICA

the mane and tail of a horse, and the hoofs and limbs of an antelope. A long beard hangs down from its chin, sometimes reaching
its knees. Its hoofs are peculiarly shaped, turning upward at the
ends. The white-tailed or black gnu, which was to be found in
the Transvaal, is practically extinct now. Another species, the
brindled gnu, largest of all gnus, standing four and one-half feet
at the shoulders, inhabits eastern and central Africa. North and
south of the Zambesi River, in herds of from ten to twenty, are
to be found the blue or brindled wildebeest, although in the dry
season when they search collectively for water holes the herds
reach as many as two or three hundred and sometimes a few
thousand.

The gnu is both timid and curious. When its curiosity is aroused
it flicks its long tail and then suddenly jumps into the air, stamps
the earth, chases another gnu around in a circle and acts, altogether, like a bull gone mad. Then, suddenly, it will grow suspicious, wheel about, kick up its heels like a donkey and, with a
swipe of its tail, go galloping away with a speed that cannot be
obtained even by a man on horseback.

THE ZEBRA—A WILD HORSE THAT REFUSES TO BE TAMED

Nature has endowed the speedy zebra with a beautifully
striped, hairy coat. Grevy's zebra has narrow stripes, and is found
frequently in the Kapiti area which is roamed by lions. In spite
of these predatory cats, the zebra is equipped to cope with its
enemies. Powerful legs, keen eyes, sensitive ears and nostrils, enable
it to avoid many enemies. Far from being cowardly, these members of the equine family have learned the lesson of co-operation.

Upon catching the scent of a stalking lion they will bunch
and await developments. With the enemy upon them they often
use their heels with startling speed and accuracy, even to the point
of beating off the lion. And then, with the lion finally driven off,
they will often wheel suddenly and gallop off at top speed. Usually, however, the lion waits downwind for a straggler, for he is
not particularly fond of being kicked about by several pairs of
zebra's heels.

Photo by A. J. Klein of the Kenya Association

ZEBRA AND GNU AT A WATERHOLE ON THE ATHI PLAINS

Zebras can be tamed and trained and broken to harness, but they are very unreliable, and therefore dangerous to the man trying to use them for farm work or for driving. They have been driven hitched to light carts and buggies, but the drivers never knew at what moment these high spirited, fleet-footed little horses would either run away or turn around and kick buggy or cart to pieces.

LARGEST OF THE REPTILES

Crocodiles and alligators, largest of the reptiles, sometimes reach a length of more than thirty feet. Only crocodiles are found in Africa, since the alligators are confined to China and the southern United States. There are only two species of alligators, but twenty-five species of other crocodilians. Probably the easiest way to distinguish between these reptiles is by the differences in the head. The crocodile has a triangular head and pointed snout, while the alligator's head is broad and the snout wide. African crocodiles, formidable as they are, do not reach the twenty-five to thirty feet attained by the Indian species.

A TRIO OF AFRICAN PYGMIES AND SMALL CROCODILE
African natives look upon the crocodile as a meat animal, and in certain parts of the Nile country he is fast disappearing.

Paul's Photos, Chicago

EVEN THE CROCODILE ENJOYS A SHOWER-BATH NOW AND THEN

These huge reptiles are well adapted for their aquatic life. Since their nostrils are near the tip of their long snouts they may float with only this part of the body above water. Almost submerged, they are able to approach an unsuspecting antelope or zebra drinking along the shore of a stream. Inactive until within striking distance, the crocodile moves with remarkable speed at close range when it seizes the prey in its huge jaws and pulls it beneath the water to drown. The crocodile has several devices which allow him to remain submerged for some time. His nostrils can be closed by valves to prevent entrance of water. In addition, the roof of the mouth and the tongue are provided with flaps which close and prevent water from entering the windpipe and lungs. Thus the crocodile can remain under water for long periods without drowning. Protected as he is with an armor of rough scales and bony plates and with such weapons as his jaws and powerful tail, the crocodile is not molested by many animals.

The food of the crocodile consists of any animals or birds that he is able to catch, or finds already dead, since he is not averse to feeding on decomposed flesh. Near villages a considerable number of domestic animals stray too near the water for their own safety. Undoubtedly many human beings have shared the fate of their cattle and dogs. It is believed that no other African wild beast has caused greater loss of human life than has the crocodile.

Perhaps the only friend of the crocodile is a species of plover, called the crocodile bird. About the size of a small crow, this species of plover will hop around the crocodile until the latter opens his mouth. While the huge mouth is open the bird hops in between those cruel jaws and picks up all the odds and ends of food, leeches and other parasites which live in the crocodile's cavernous mouth. This bird will also walk all over the crocodile's back, legs, and feet picking off water parasites.

ANIMALS OF THE NAIROBI COUNTRY

Nairobi, jumping-off place for parties of game hunters and explorers, lies about three hundred and forty miles inland from Mombasa. There is some native agriculture in the Nairobi country,

Courtesy American Museum of Natural History

AFRICAN WART HOG, SOMETIMES CALLED THE GIANT FOREST PIG

especially near the Uganda Railway. The region is essentially a mixture of jungle and plains, wild and untamed. Big game sometimes obstructs the passage of trains, even causing wrecks.

One of the first animals to be seen in the hinterland around and about Kijabe is a species of civet cat that barks like a dog. He is generally known as the meerkat. The meerkat is related to the cobra-defying mongoose of India and Egypt, and is not commonly found as far north in Africa as Kijabe. He is not much more than a foot in length, and his long soft fur is of a grizzled greyish color. The meerkats are burrowers with unusually long claws on their front feet. They feed primarily on roots, but also on occasion eat small birds, birds' eggs, young chicks, grubs, and other insects. Like most animals, the meerkat can adapt itself to changing conditions in that in one region it might be largely insectivorous, while in another region it would subsist on roots, bulbs, and birds. Meerkats are gregarians, and their burrows are grouped together somewhat like the "prairie dog towns" of the western United States.

One of the ugliest of animals is the wart hog, a striking contrast to the graceful eland which lives in the same region. Generally speaking, the wart hog looks like a large pig, the foreparts of which are covered with fairly long bristles, while the rear quarters are almost hairless. The appearance of the head is certainly such as to impress one that here is a fierce and dangerous animal. The face is broad and flat, and there are conical warts beneath the eyes, and between the eyes and the tusks. The enormous, incurved tusks may exceed a foot in length. His actions, however, belie his appearance, for under ordinary circumstances the wart hogs are not fierce and use their tusks only to dig roots. However, if attacked by a dog, the wart hog is capable of ably defending himself and may inflict very severe wounds with a few slashing strokes of his vicious tusks.

Like the domesticated pig, the wart hog likes the water and mud puddles; therefore he is usually found along the swampy and reedy places on lakes and streams. Being fleet of foot, he will run away from danger if possible, but will fight if necessary. When chased, he frequently looks for an aardvark den in which to hide. Although heading straight for it at considerable speed, upon arrival at the entrance to the hole he will reverse himself quickly and go in backward. The females and the young travel together, but the boars are doomed to a somewhat lonely existence.

If he were at all sensitive about his lack of beauty, the wart hog would be consoled by contemplating the rhinoceros. The location of this monstrous beast may at times be revealed by the tick or rhinoceros birds, which feed on insects, grubs, and other morsels from the rhino's thick hide. When danger threatens, these birds warn their host by running around his head; flapping their wings and screeching loudly before they take refuge in nearby trees. When these signals have been duly impressed upon him, the rhino usually trots a few yards, then stops to make a cursory investigation. He is a bit stupid, however, so his fear will soon subside,

Courtesy Field Museum of Natural History

WHITE RHINOCEROS—NOT REALLY WHITE, BUT SMOKY GRAY

and his rather poor eyesight will not be of much aid in discerning the enemy. When the lumbering rhinoceros decides definitely to flee, he can easily outrun a man. Even horses are forced to break into a fast gallop to overtake him.

There are five species of rhinoceros in the world, three in Asia and two in Africa. The "white rhino" of the Uganda region is about five feet eight inches high and may weigh two and one half tons or so. This is the largest land mammal now living with the exception of the elephant. The black rhinoceros is smaller in size, but is probably the most ferocious and dangerous of the rhinos. The horns differ in structure from those of most animals. They are formed of a great number of bristles of hair packed close together. The front horn is perhaps about two feet in length, and sloping backward, while the rear horn is just about a foot long, conical in shape, and usually straight. The skin of the black rhino is not folded like that of the Indian species; nevertheless it is unusually tough, and along the back and rump is quite often more than an inch in thickness. Although the natives in the Kijabe country are partial to rhino meat, the average white hunter would rather eat the meat of the eland, for rhino meat is often coarse, dry, and tough.

THE AWESOME PYTHON

West of Victoria Nyanza lies the fearsome Lake Chohoa country which is inhabited by cannibals. This region has numerous lakes and streams, and pythons that measure up to twenty-five feet in length. Even this monster is smaller than the Asiatic python, specimens of which have been known to exceed thirty-three feet. The Nile python resembles the species found in the Lake Chohoa region, but is somewhat smaller.

When trailing one of the smaller antelopes, the python usually creeps up and seizes a hind leg. Instantly the rest of his body is a whirl of action as he tries to wrap as many folds as possible around his prey. If the animal falls down on its side, the python is checkmated for a while, but he will wait with patience. Sooner or later the animal will move and the big snake will take full advantage of his opportunity.

The python is non-venomous, and kills his prey by coiling himself tightly about it. He then squeezes, breaks, and kneads the

Paul's Photos, Chicago

THIS PYTHON'S BREAKFAST CONSISTED OF 300 POUNDS OF ANTELOPE
Several weeks will pass before his prehensile body returns to its normal size.

carcass until it is suitable for swallowing. During this kneading process all of the bones are broken. The kneading process requires much less time with small prey such as the rabbit or animals of similar size. They are broken somewhat, of course, but do not require as much preparation as would a sheep, pig, or one of the smaller African antelopes.

Having crushed and squashed the small antelope, let us say, the python then moistens the broken mass with his own saliva. Here and there he guides the dribbling fluid until the meal is fairly well covered. This done he prepares to swallow it whole, beginning with the head. As he gets this big piece in his mouth, the python disjoints his jaws. This act enlarges the throat considerably and enables the python to swallow animals that are two and three times his own diameter. Although certain throat and head muscles are of some help, the swallowing is brought about largely by the teeth, which are strong and sharp and well rooted in the roof of the mouth and in the jaws. Moreover, they are curved backward toward the throat. Sinking these sharp teeth into the prey, the python then works his body muscles in such a way as to pull himself over his meal.

GORILLA PARADISE

Splendid specimens of gorillas are to be seen in zoos and museums, but the age-old argument about the existence of these apes was settled only a few years ago. Long before Columbus discovered America, a wandering priest returned to Spain with stories about huge primates with hairy bodies, long arms, and short legs. His amazed hearers refused to believe this astonishing account, and the priest was threatened with torture if he persisted in telling such absurd and preposterous yarns.

The first white man to make a comprehensive report on these apes in recent times was an English sailor, one Andrew Battel, who had the misfortune to be the only survivor of a shipwreck off the Angola coast some time in the year 1592. He was taken prisoner by a band of raiding Negroes and carried far inland deep

Black Star photo by William Fox

YOUNG GORILLA IN PROFOUND MEDITATION
We wonder just what is on his mind. Note the resemblance of the big
toe to the human thumb.

into the Luango country. Some years later he managed to escape and found his way back to England where he attracted considerable attention with the accounts of his adventures.

In these accounts he gave good descriptions of what his Negro captors called the "Engeco," the animal now known to us as the bright and intelligent chimpanzee. Moreover, he gave a good description of a larger and stronger animal, known to the natives as the "Pongo," now called the gorilla. About the year 1613, this narrator published a book in which he went into considerable detail concerning these two little-known animals. Sad to say, the "wise ones" of the time laughed at Andrew Battel's tales. He was simply a gifted prevaricator, they said, but more than two hundred and fifty years later it was discovered that the English sailor had told the truth. Even the most skeptical were convinced when an English showman toured Europe with a monkey he advertised as a chimpanzee, and this chimpanzee was later fully identified as the animal we now know as the gorilla.

Less than one hundred miles north of Kisenji, at the north end of Lake Kivu, there is a region that is famous not only for its old volcanoes, but also because it is the home of the largest

"BUSHMAN," THE FAMOUS NINE-YEAR-OLD GORILLA OF LINCOLN PARK ZOO, CHICAGO

Courtesy Chicago Park District

and finest specimens of gorillas. Between the extinct volcanic peaks of Mount Mikeno and Mount Karisimbi stretches a rocky ridge or "backbone." On the lower slopes of both ridge and volcanoes, slopes buried deep under thick forests of bamboo and hagenia trees, a few elephants, lions, and buffaloes are found. In a certain more or less restricted area at the Mount Mikeno end, however, is the gorilla region.

Compared to other African animals, the gorilla ranges over a rather small and somewhat restricted area in the dense forests of equatorial Africa, where very few other large animals are found. The gorilla is easily the largest and most formidable of the anthropoid apes. Ranging between five and six feet in height when full grown and in good physical condition, he attains a weight of over five hundred pounds and is exceptionally strong. The gorilla can hardly be said to have a neck, for the compact head appears to grow out from the upper part of his grey-skinned hairless chest. Low-browed, with his keen eyes set back under protruding ridges of bone, and with great open jaws that show strong canine tusks, he presents a fearful, awesome aspect that at once strikes terror even to the boldest hunter. His legs are short and muscular, with a big toe that functions like a human thumb. The arms, however, are much longer. A specimen with a standing height of five feet six inches is likely to have an arm-spread of almost eight feet, including a chest-width ranging from twenty-five to thirty inches in a large specimen. Such powerful arms make the gorilla an extremely dangerous and formidable foe at close quarters. With his stubby hands and fingers he can break a man's arm or leg with as much ease as human hands and fingers can break a match, so great is his strength. Gorillas vary in color from iron gray to deep brown-black, while the hair on the head has a slightly reddish tinge. The older gorillas can be distinguished from the younger ones by their more grizzled iron-gray hair around the jaws and the lower abdominal parts of the body. The broad chest, however, is hairless.

A decade or so ago it was believed that all gorillas lived in trees, and it is possible that in some areas such is the case. However, it is now known that gorillas are primarily ground dwellers. Because of their large size, they are poorly adapted for an arboreal life. It is usually stated that they are active during the day, wandering about in search of food. At night the females and young sleep on platforms built of branches, while the males remain on guard at the base of the tree. These sleeping platforms are usually occupied for one night only. Sleeping with their backs against the tree trunks, gorillas are in a position to protect themselves from prowling beasts. This does not mean that they have many natural enemies, but hungry lions and leopards have been known to make attempts upon the gorilla, often getting the worst of it. Usually, however, these big cats do not live in the gorilla country, although there are times when they come together by accident.

The families usually consist of a male, several females, and probably one or two young ones. Of course, there are exceptions to this rule, for two males have been seen in the same group. In spite of the fact that the quite noticeable canine teeth indicate the flesh-eater, the gorilla is largely herbivorous. Although he helps himself to birds and bird's eggs now and then, he is perhaps more partial to wild plums, berries, nuts, bananas, and bamboo shoots. Those who have studied the gorilla in the Mikeno country state that these apes live largely upon bamboo shoots in that region.

The gorilla walks on all fours, with his hands doubled under. At the approach of danger, however, he rears up on his hind feet, raises his head, and as he beats his expansive chest with his great fists, emits a series of grunts, roars, and snarls that strike terror to all within hearing.

CHIMPANZEE

There are also a few very fine specimens of chimpanzee in the Kasindi region. Like his cousin, the gorilla, the chimpanzee has been the basis of considerable fable and folklore. Early explorers reported having seen frightfully ugly, hairy, and misshapen "human" beings in Africa's equatorial forests, but we have come to know that these ugly, hairy, forest-dwellers are the chimpanzees. They are similar to the gorilla in physique, except that their bodies are smaller and their chests are narrower. The full-

Courtesy Chicago Park District
"CHILLO," THE EIGHTEEN-YEAR-OLD CHIMPANZEE IN LINCOLN
PARK ZOO, CHICAGO

grown chimpanzee weighs about one hundred fifty pounds, is about five feet in height and has an arm-spread a foot longer. The brownish-black hair is short, the head is round and the ears large. His diet consists largely of fruits, nuts, and certain insects. In some sections they live and sleep on the ground, while in other places they build large nests in the trees.

Perhaps the most interesting and intriguing thing about the average chimpanzee is that, in more ways than one, he is almost human. He has shown us that he is capable of thinking things out, especially when it is necessary for him to pile up boxes in order to get at some bananas hanging beyond his normal reach. Chimpanzees are the most intelligent of the apes. There are, at present, several well-educated chimpanzees, and prominent among them is the female "Tarzana," which has been trained to do many interesting tricks.

Courtesy Chicago Park District
AFRICAN BABOON—NOTE THE DOG-LIKE FACE

BABOONS AND OTHER MONKEYS

A very interesting group of Old World monkeys inhabiting Africa and Arabia are known as baboons. They are of large size and are covered with long, dark hair. They are chiefly distinguished by the elongated, blunt muzzle, with the nostrils in the end, giving the face in profile the appearance of a dog. The presence of large canine teeth, which the males use as very effective weapons, heightens the resemblance to a dog. The tail is of medium length and the buttocks are brilliantly colored. Although they could be classified as omnivorous, they are mainly flesh-eaters and prefer small rodents and birds to larger game. Baboons often follow herds of elephants and wild boars through the jungle and feed on insects, earthworms, scorpions, and roots which are uncovered by these animals as they uproot many plants.

In West Africa, the largest of the baboons, the mandrill, dwells in the forests. The enormous head of the mandrill is crested and bearded, and the muzzle is blue in color. The crimson color of the bare buttocks shades off into a deep blue. The mandrill has its home in rocky, wooded country, but his food consists largely of fruits, bulbs, snakes, lizards, frogs, and numerous insects, including the scorpions. Generally speaking, the mandrill is more even-tempered and tractable than other baboons, although when forced into battle he can be just as ferocious and dangerous.

Another species of baboon is the chacma of South Africa, sometimes called the dog-faced or pig-faced baboon. He is a muscular fellow, sometimes attaining the size of a large mastiff. With his teeth and his muscular arms and feet he can make any two dogs fight for their very lives. The chacma is particularly noted for craft and cunning when rustling for food, especially when raiding fruit and corn crops near settlements. When the raid begins only a few of the oldest and wiliest chacmas do the actual stealing, while the remainder of the group arrange themselves in a line like the old-time bucket-brigade firemen. Having

Courtesy American Museum of Natural History

AFRICAN MANDRILL IN BELLIGER-
ENT POSE—NOTE THE TUSKS

Courtesy New York Zoölogical Society

THE CHACMA BABOON FROM
SOUTH AFRICA

cut the fruit or corn with their sharp teeth, the raiders pass the food back along the line, keeping it up until all of them have something to eat. Not only do they eat their fill, but they also stuff their rather large cheek-pouches for another meal when a sharp lookout is not so necessary. Thus, when they have finished their raid they retire into the rocky haunts again, their distended cheek-pouches making them appear more like lions than monkeys.

Farther north, in Morocco and across the Mediterranean on the rock of Gibraltar, is the tailless Barbary ape, one of the monkeys known as the macaque. He is light yellowish in color, except for his face, which is hairless and has a pink cast. He is very abundant in some parts of North Africa, inhabiting rocky mountains and woods.

Away to the northeast of this great continent we find the green, vervet, and grivet monkeys. The first, as its name implies, has fur of an olive-greenish hue, hence its name. The grivet is similarly colored, while the vervet, which is found in the south, is distinguished from the "green" monkeys by a rusty patch of hair around the root of the tail, and also by its black hands and feet.

THE LEMURS

The lemurs are the most primitive of the primates. They do not resemble the monkeys very closely in appearance yet are related to them. They do have an opposable thumb and therefore a grasping hand, a characteristic in common with the monkeys. An interesting characteristic of the lemur family is their enormous, luminous eyes that glisten like highly-polished discs of gray marble. In the daytime, when these animals are stupefied by the light, the pupils become a thin black slit surrounded by brown or gray or yellow. But in the night, when the lemur becomes active and moves rapidly through the trees like a disembodied ghost, the pupils dilate to their full size. In fact, the name "lemur" means a ghost, and the natives of Madagascar, where the true lemur ranges, believe that these quiet, wraithlike animals flitting noiselessly through the jungles, are spirits of dead human beings. They are not all nocturnal, however, for the ring-tailed and

Courtesy Dr. Frank P. Thompson, Chicago

AN AFRICAN BULL BUFFALO ENJOYING HIS MIDDAY REST

Courtesy The Art Institute of Chicago

AFRICAN BUFFALOES COOLING OFF IN THE SACRED LAKE
AT KARNAK, EGYPT

ruffed lemurs are active during the day, and others acquire the habit very easily.

Another characteristic of all lemurs is their soft, beautifully-colored fur with the same resilient pile as a chinchilla's fur. This is essential because lemurs are sensitive to cold and usually huddle together for communal warmth. On the Madagascar and Comoro Islands, where most of the true lemurs are to be found, various species exist, particularly the ring-tailed, the sportive, the weasel, the gray, the mouse, the crowned, the coquerel and the black and white lemurs. Although most of them are scarcely the size of a cat, their voices are deep-throated and as haunting as an owl's and a group of them sound like a troop of angry ghouls. The black and white lemur, especially, can be tamed and domesticated.

The galagos, which are not true lemurs but are lemuroids, can be found only on the mainland of Africa. It, too, has the immense lemur eyes and the soft, lustrous brown fur. Its ears are thin and hairless and can be folded up like a beetle's wings. The Maholi galagos and Garnett's galagos are two additional species of lemuroids to be found in Africa. The slender loris, the tarsier and other lemuroids will be discussed in the Malay and Indian sections of this book.

WATER BUFFALO

As we push northward from the Kisenji country, following the Ruchuru River, we get glimpses of the renowned African buffalo and hippopotamus. The buffalo is not particularly numerous in this region, and he has slight physical differences when compared with the species ranging the southern part of Africa. At any rate, the species found north of Kisenji is larger than the average ox and is distinguished by the strong, broad-based, solid horns that appear to lie flat across the top of his head, the ends curling upward like a certain kind of bicycle handle-bars.

Ferocious, cunning, and quick of movement, the water buffalo has a massive head and horns which combine to make him a formidable battering ram. With a weight that may exceed sixteen hundred pounds, the water buffalo can plunge through what looks like impenetrable thickets and jungle tangles. Needless to say, his hide is thick and tough, and wise natives farther south know only too well that the buffalo hide makes the finest and strongest harness. These animals graze and feed on the plains and in swampy places along river and lakes. In hot weather they spend most of their time wallowing in the mud and water in order to prevent loss of too much body water by evaporation. Cooler weather finds them out in the open. They have few enemies except the lion and man.   The mature animals, however, can hold off the lion and sometimes manage to gore or cripple him badly. The younger, smaller buffaloes, however, occasionally succumb to the lion after a valiant fight. Some idea of the mature buffalo's enormous strength can be gained from the fact that he has been known to charge a mounted hunter, and, with head and horns, lift man and horse clear off the ground before throwing them to one side.

HIPPOPOTAMUS

The hippo seldom wanders far from water. He spends most of his time along the water's edge, or out in the depths where he walks around on the bottom and where he feeds on his favorite

Courtesy American Museum of Natural History
AFRICAN HIPPOPOTAMUS
Sometimes referred to as the "River Horse" in spite of the fact that his closest relative is the pig.

aquatic plants and grasses. He can stay under water as long as seven or eight minutes, but his usual time is about three or four minutes. Although this ponderous animal is often referred to as the "river horse," his closest relative is the pig. A mature and well-developed hippopotamus will measure between twelve and fourteen feet in length and about four or five feet in height from the toes to the top of the shoulders. Weighing more than three tons, an adult hippo is a formidable antagonist when aroused. The upper lip is thick and bulging, and the ears are unusually small. The skin is two inches thick in places and covers flesh which Africans enjoy eating.

A mild and inoffensive animal unless forced to do battle, the hippo is as dangerous as a wounded "rogue" elephant. When first aroused, he will gallop rapidly back and forth, snorting, bellowing, and grunting. If disturbed when in the water, he will very likely charge boat and occupants, scattering them right and left and causing considerable panic and damage. In spite of his bulk, he is quick in movement both on land and in the water.

ELEPHANTS—GIANTS OF THE ANIMAL KINGDOM

Few animals appeal to the imagination as does the ponderous African bull elephant. His enormous bulk, expansive ears, legs like small tree trunks, tiny eyes, and swinging trunk never fail to attract and hold attention. One of the finest elephant ranges in all Africa is the region around Lake Edward in Uganda. Dense forests of acacias and palms cover the country, from which have come some of the largest elephants ever taken for museums. One specimen, the internationally famous "Jolly Jumbo," measured ten feet, seven inches at the shoulder and weighed ten thousand pounds. "Jolly Jumbo" was killed by a freight train in Woodstock, Ontario, but the train was almost as badly smashed as the elephant. Another specimen from the Lake Edward country is now on exhibition in the South Kensington Museum in England. It was eleven feet, four inches in height and weighed thirteen thousand pounds when killed. Its length was thirty feet, including an eight-foot trunk and a tail five and one-half feet long. The back feet were twenty inches in diameter, the front feet seventeen inches. The ears, like huge, thick wings, measured fifty-

Paul's Photos, Chicago

TWO OLD VETERANS OF THE CONGO TALK THINGS OVER
(African elephants.)

six inches in diameter. All of these measurements were taken in the field when this big bull was brought down, and they were followed by taxidermists whose chief ambition was to mount this enormous animal as lifelike as possible. It should be mentioned, too, that this particular specimen was "skinned out" all in one piece, and hundreds of natives worked and slaved for weeks to carry it down to the railhead for shipment to England. Before it was shipped, the ton or so of two-inch elephant hide was given a thorough coating with ordinary castor oil which not only kept the myriads of insects at bay, but also kept the thick skin soft and pliable and ready for the taxidermist's hands.

On the average, a bull's tusks will weigh about fifty or sixty pounds each. The heaviest known tusks weigh a little over two hundred pounds each and are more than ten feet in length. Tusks are really teeth, long incisors that continue to develop until they protrude several feet from the base of the jaw. Where they fit

Courtesy South African Railways
BULL ELEPHANT IN HIS OWN AFRICAN BACK YARD

into the jawbone, tusks are hollow, but the portions outside of the mouth are solid ivory, and worth as much as ten dollars a pound. Both sexes of the African elephant have tusks, but in the Asiatic or Indian species the female's tusks are very small and rarely grow very far out from under the lower lip. Barring accidents, the average African bull elephant will develop a pair of fine tusks. Hard use may result in these long teeth being disfigured, blunted, or even broken.

The powerful trunk that swings between the ivory tusks is an interesting and unusual nose. The trunk of the Indian species is smooth, while that of the African is a mass of wrinkles and corrugations, and is much longer. At the tip of the trunk of the Indian species, the trunk tapers off into a sort of "finger," while at the tip of the African's trunk there are two such "fingers." These little protuberances are really "fingers" in the way they are used, for with these fleshy digits these ponderous animals can pick up blades of grass, stalks of hay, and even such a thing as a small glass bead. Naturally, these "fingers" are of great service in procuring fruits and leaves and shoots that constitute part of the animal's menu.

It is not unusual to see a bull and two or three cows feeding on acacia and palm leaves. Their movements are slow and deliberate as they move from one feeding place to another. The bull leads the group in this leisurely foraging, which may continue for hours. When their seemingly insatiable appetites have been satisfied, the elephants sleep standing up. It is a rare occasion, indeed, when an African elephant is found dozing or sleeping lying down. The reclining position is assumed, of course, when these mountains of flesh and bone indulge in a bath in mud or water, or when they dust themselves beside some great anthill.

Once an enemy has been discovered, the bull's ears stand stiffly at right angles to his huge head. The wrinkled and corrugated trunk stretches out to a point in the direction of danger. Two tubes in the trunk lead to remarkably sensitive nerves of smell located where the trunk merges with the head. If reassured that the intruder means no harm, the great bull will relax and continue feeding, perhaps moving off slowly into the jungle with his wards in the lead. The source of danger is located by the senses of smell and hearing, since the elephant's eyes are of service only at close range. An unusual feature concerning a herd on the move is that the pace is usually set by one of the smaller females. She will set the pace and seemingly set the course in such a manner that the smallest of the herd can keep up with the main group. The bull seldom takes the lead on the "run away" for he would move too fast and would soon be separated from his herd.

The gestation period of the elephant is between eighteen and twenty-two months, and the calf may weigh about two hundred and fifty pounds and stand about three feet in height. The mammary glands are between the front legs of the mother, and at feeding time the little fellow folds his tiny trunk back over his forehead and helps himself with his peculiar mouth.

The baby is protected and watched over by all members of

the herd. All the adults seem to feel that they have a share in him and are responsible for his general welfare and safety. Meanwhile, the little fellow moves about underneath, pushing and shoving his way between their legs and under their huge bellies, screaming and whinnying and enjoying himself immensely. Months later, as breast feeding tapers off, the calf is introduced to fruits, leaves, barks, roots, and the taste of the sap of certain trees. In captivity, however, the elephant's diet consists largely of hay and vegetables, and plenty of good water.

Although both the Asiatic and African species can be tamed and put to work, the smaller Indian or Asiatic is much preferred, perhaps because it is more even-tempered than the African. Moreover, the hollow behind the head of the Indian species provides, perhaps, a better "point of control" from which to handle these huge beasts. At any rate, about the only reason advanced for the predominance of the Indian species as a work elephant is that it is just a little more tractable and even-tempered than

Courtesy Chicago Park District

WEST AFRICAN PYGMY ELEPHANT
The West African Pygmy is not a separate species of African elephant. He is
merely the smallest of the family.

the African. The so-called "pygmy" elephants of West Africa are not "pygmies" at all. They are small, however, as compared to most individuals of the African species, because they seldom attain a shoulder height of more than six or seven feet. Besides this lower stature, their ears are correspondingly smaller than the larger individuals previously described. Even though there are differences in size, the African elephants are regarded as the same species. The so-called white elephants that now and then come to light in India and Asia are really albinos of the common species, just as in America we have albino squirrels and, now and then, an albino woodchuck or groundhog. The so-called white elephant is held sacred in Siam, and during the American War between the States, the king of Siam offered President Lincoln four of these white elephants to help win the war for the Union. President Lincoln, however, could not see his way clear to accept this very kind offer.

Slow-moving and slow-eating, elephants live a sort of leisurely life and that, perhaps, explains why they live so long. The African species reaches maturity at about thirty years of age, and it is a matter of record that both Asiatic and African specimens have lived in captivity for one hundred and thirty years.

INSECTS—TO BE EATEN OR FEARED

The ponderous elephants, hippopotamuses, buffaloes, and other animals make the Lake Edward region of great interest to the student of natural history, but at the other end of the scale, for instance in insect life, there are equally important and strange species demanding our attention.

Often at great distances swarms of millions of kungu flies appear like great, black storm clouds. Though they do not bite or sting, everyone in their path attempts to avoid them, for the myriads of fluttering creatures find their way into ears, eyes, nostrils, and mouth. As they pass, they fall to the ground in great quantities as members of the swarm die or drop from exhaustion. In this way they prove a boon to the cannibalistic Bahunis and Wakopis who inhabit the western shore of Lake Edward. These weird jungle peoples gather kungu flies in great baskets, add a little flour, and make patties or cakes upon which they have a

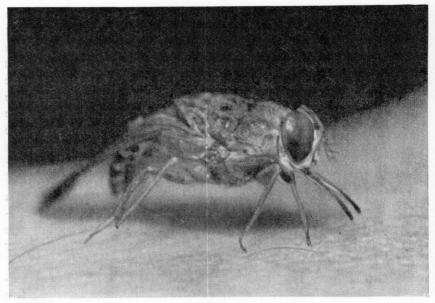

Paul's Photos, Chicago

THE TSETSE FLY—SCOURGE OF AFRICA

This is the fly that carries the germs of the deadly sleeping sickness, dangerous not only
to black and white men, but also to many African animals.

great feast. Although the kungu fly is at least useful as food
for the natives, neither man nor beast has anything but dislike
and fear for another insect of equatorial Africa—the dreaded
tsetse fly. This insect, the carrier of the sleeping-sickness germ,
looks like a rather large housefly, and is a dull mouse-grey in color.
Generally speaking, the average specimen is a little more than
half an inch in length, although another eighth of an inch is
added by the stiff "beak" that projects straight forward from
the middle of the head. Its bite is exceptionally dangerous to
whites and blacks alike. Many explorers and missionaries have
been seriously infected, and in some regions tribes of native jungle
peoples have been almost wiped out by the havoc caused by the
tsetse fly. Human beings are not the only ones that die from
sleeping sickness as a result of the bite of this fly, for it is fatal
also to many wild animals, and horses often are unable to enter the
fly-infested regions.

TERMITES—BUILDERS OF INSECT SOCIETIES

On every hand in the tropical regions of the world are evidences of the wonderful architectural skill of the termites, or "white ants" as they are erroneously called. And yet few visitors to these regions ever see the insects themselves, for the great majority of them are blind, wingless, and do not expose their pale, thin-skinned bodies to the light and air very often.

In the open savanna regions of Africa one may frequently observe mounds, built by these insects, which are so large and numerous as to resemble a village of native huts at a distance. These astonishing earthen structures are more or less conical, columnar, wedge-shaped or mushroom-shaped, and may attain a height of eighteen to twenty feet.

In forested regions the nests are usually built in the trees and may attain the size of a barrel. These tree nests are composed of digested wood excreted by the termites and fashioned by them into a specific shape. The termites often construct rather com-

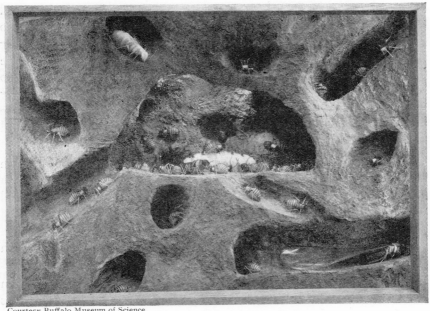

Courtesy Buffalo Museum of Science
COLONY OF AFRICAN TERMITES

Courtesy Dr. Frank P. Thompson, Chicago

"APARTMENT HOUSE" OF THE
AFRICAN TERMITES

plicated rain-shedding devices over their nests in the tropical rain forests.

Even though travelers are impressed by the sight of these architectural wonders, very few contemplate the efficient social organization existing within the mound that made this possible. A complete census, if that were possible, of one of these large mounds would reveal a population of hundreds of thousands of individuals. It is estimated that the largest of these societies may consist of well over a million termites.

A cursory examination of this society would reveal that the individuals are not all alike and have different social functions to perform. A more thorough study would reveal the following organization. In the center of the large mound is located the special royal chamber in which the queen of the colony grows to an enormous size. She is fed by the worker termites until her abdomen becomes greatly distended by the egg sacs and fat. She may attain a size four inches in length and be twenty thousand times the volume of a single worker.

The queen is too large to move about and too well taken care of by the workers to need to move. The sole task of the queen is to lay eggs which she does at the rate of about thirty thousand a day. At this astonishing rate a queen will deposit about ten million eggs a year; and the estimated life of a queen is ten years. This is undoubtedly the most incredible egg-laying machine in the animal kingdom.

The king lives in the royal cell also. The termites differ from the ants in having a king, for the queen ant is a widow and does not have a royal consort.

The "subjects" of the royal pair are members of either the worker caste or the soldier caste. It is of interest to note that all of the members of the colony are the progeny of the royal pair. The duties of the workers are to construct and repair the nest, and to feed the royal pair, the soldiers and the young termites. The soldiers differ from the workers in having large mandibles or other defensive mechanism, and their duty is to guard against invasion if possible.

At certain times of the year, many of the young termites develop into dark-bodied, winged individuals. These winged forms leave the parent colony and fly away to establish new colonies. They pair off, lose their wings, excavate a small chamber in the ground, and the female begins to lay eggs. The workers which develop from these eggs then take up the labors of the colony and a vast society is in time established.

Termites have an insatiable appetite for wood, which they consume in great quantities. Structures built of wood are unsafe in the warmer regions of the world and consequently, houses, furniture, fences, telegraph poles, bridges, railway ties, and even books do not escape the mandibles of these small insects. The damage done throughout the world is inestimable. It is believed that in the United States alone the property damage may exceed $40,-000,000 annually.

TERMITE ENEMIES

It is no wonder that several of the large mammals in different parts of the world have taken advantage of the endless supply of food present in the termite nests of the tropics. Since these soft-bodied insects have no defense against animals much larger than themselves, they furnish an ideal source of food.

It is amazing, however, that the bodies of these "ant" eaters have been so wonderfully adapted for this specialized feeding habit. The anteaters of tropical America, the spiny anteater of Australia, the scaly anteater (pangolin) of Africa and the Orient, and the aardvark of Africa, have structural characteristics which fit them for this method of feeding, yet they are not closely related animals at all.

They all have very well-developed claws on their forefeet for opening the termite nests, long tubular snouts, and long, thin, very flexible tongues to which the termites adhere.

THE AARDVARK

One of the strangest animals in Africa is the "earth pig," which competes with the wart hog for the dubious honor of being the continent's ugliest animal. The aardvark is strikingly unlike any other living animal. At first, it may appear to be somewhat pig-like in appearance, but this resemblance is very superficial. It possesses a heavy body, short legs, a long, thick, muscular tail, and a long snout. Its ears are large and somewhat rabbit-like in appearance. The aardvark uses its very heavy, somewhat hoof-like claws for burrowing, and when threatened by larger animals, can bury itself quickly and seems to "pull the hole in after it." Natives, who are very fond of the aardvark's tasty flesh, know better than to try to dig it out. Even if the diggers chance to catch the hind legs of the aardvark when it is but halfway in the burrow, it would take the combined strength of three or four men to pull it out, so solidly can it anchor itself with those muscular front legs and strange claw-hoofs.

When the aardvark is hungry, it selects a termite mound and goes to work with its forefeet to excavate a hole near the base

Courtesy American Museum of Natural History

THE AFRICAN AARDVARK OR "EARTH PIG"

large enough for its tubular snout. As the internal part of the termite nest is exposed, and the quiet routine of the society disturbed, thousands of termites mill about in utter confusion. Immediately, the long, elastic tongue, covered with sticky saliva, weaves back and forth carrying a hundred or so termites into the mouth at a time. The aardvark differs from the remainder of the "anteaters" in possessing teeth. It is doubtful whether they have any real use. Strange as it seems, it not only gets fat and strong on a diet of termites but its flesh is exceptionally tasty. Because of the desirability of the meat, and a hide that makes the finest of leather, the aardvark has been so steadily hunted that it is now difficult to find one in regions where there once were many. This North African species is a bit smaller than the extreme southern variety.

THE SCALY ANTEATER (PANGOLIN)

This curious animal also feeds on termites, but bears very little resemblance to the aardvark. In many respects it looks like an animated pine cone because of its wonderful armor of large overlapping, horny scales. These scales are formed by the fusing together of fine hairs. They form an excellent means of defense, for when the pangolin rolls into a ball when attacked, these sharp scales project at right angles to the body. They also aid in climbing trees, those of the under surface serving as climbing hooks. These animals are said to descend from trees by deliberately dropping, depending on their armor to protect them.

Scaly anteaters, like the other anteaters, have long, worm-like tongues for capturing insects. Furthermore, they are toothless like the American anteaters, to which they are not closely related.

LITTLE-KNOWN JUNGLE ANIMALS

Along with the familiar animals which we see in every circus and zoo, the equatorial African jungle has inhabitants rarely seen or heard, and the aardwolf, meaning "earth wolf," is certainly one of these. At first glance it looks like a small striped hyena, and belongs to the same family, but its muzzle and ears are much sharper and it has a stiff well-developed mane. It is called the earth wolf because it digs and lives in underground burrows, and its diet consists largely of carrion, termites and other insects. The tiny fennec-fox makes his home here, too. His ears are almost as large as human hands in spite of the fact that he is less than twenty inches in length, and a bit short-legged in the bargain. He is a cute little fellow, and lives largely on fruits, rodents, and insects.

The ratel, sometimes called the honey badger, gets his nickname because of his fondness for honey. Although he is called a "bear" he is, perhaps, more closely related to the badgers, which he resembles in size. His grayish-white back fur gives him the mark of the badger, while the black fur on legs and belly is much the same as that found on an ordinary black bear cub. The ratel or honey badger is omnivorous, living largely upon insects, small snakes and wild honey, with a meal of fresh meat now and then. He is largely nocturnal, and spends his days sleeping high up in the trees. Like the common bears of America, he is passionately fond of honey. Like them, too, the ratel will chew and rip and tear away at a wild beehive until he reaches the sweets. Being loose-skinned and well-furred, he takes his time as he works toward the honey, even though he is smothered with outraged bees. About the only spot where they might sting him is at the tip of his nose, and he is careful that the bees don't come to a halt on that particularly sensitive spot.

THE JERBOA AND PHARAOH'S RAT

Aristotle mentions a small animal that "walks on its hind legs," while Pliny, evidently writing about the same animal, describes it as a "walking biped." In more modern times this miniature "kangaroo" has been named the jerboa. These peculiar creatures usually travel in small groups. Because their tawny color merges so well with grass and foliage, they are best seen while making prodigious leaps. Although they are no larger than ordinary rats, these marvelous jumpers can cover eight feet in one leap. The bounds are made so quickly that the eye can barely catch sight of the tiny forefeet touching the ground. Their long tails, tufted at

Courtesy American Museum of Natural History

THE AFRICAN JERBOA OR "KANGAROO RAT"

He is not much larger than an ordinary warehouse rat, and when our grandfathers attended school it was believed that the jerboa was really a miniature kangaroo. We now know him to be a member of the rodent family.

the end, are much longer than their bodies, and without them they are just about helpless, for the tails act as balancers when jumping. Deprived of their tails, the jerboas are unable to jump and easily fall prey to some predatory fox or jungle cat. The jerboa, or kangaroo rat, has a body length of about six inches, and a tufted tail more than seven inches long. He is a burrowing animal, and his diet consists largely of bulbs, roots, fruits, grain, and bark. Near the settlements this jerboa does tremendous damage to crops, for he is exceptionally well equipped with powerful jaws and strong chisel-like front teeth. There are a few other species in the dry desert areas, and in certain parts of Barbary they are quite numerous. Although he is often referred to as a "kangaroo" rat, the jerboa is really a rodent and is not related to the true kangaroo in any way. His New World relative is the jumping mouse of North America.

Pharaoh's rat is a weasel-like animal that may be seen as he scurries down to a stream to get a drink and then darts back into the underbrush. Wild or tame, he is a rather useful animal, because he is very fond of snakes, mice, rats, birds and birds' eggs, insects, and scorpions. Because of this diet, it will be seen at once that he would be a rather useful adjunct to the Egyptian households in the outlying agricultural districts, for he is worth half a dozen house cats when it comes to keeping homes and sheds and barns clear of all kinds of pests. When he has just about cleaned up the vermin in the homes and sheds, however, he becomes a nuisance because of a predilection for poultry.

SHIPS OF THE DESERT

In the more settled portions of Egypt we find an animal that has undoubtedly played an important part in the economic life of man. This animal is the camel which is characterized by either one or two humps. Long before man learned to print books, ancient scribes mentioned the camel in both poetry and prose. For instance, camels are mentioned in the Bible in Genesis and Judges, and in the first book of Job we learn that Job's "substance" consisted of "three thousand camels." In spite of his usefulness and his importance as a burden bearer, in the eleventh chapter of Leviticus the camel is outlawed because he has a cloven hoof and also because he chews the cud.

The camel is one of the largest ruminants, with an average over-all length of between ten and twelve feet, and a height of about seven feet at the top of the head or the hump. The dromedary, distinguished by his single hump, is generally known as the Arabian camel. Although he is as tall as the Egyptian two-humped camel he is lighter in build and is the speedier runner of the two. Like the two-humped camel, the dromedary is a beast of burden and a special harness is needed to secure the load to his single-humped back.

The camel's lot is a hard one. Patient and strong, he goes on his way enduring thirst, hunger, and abuse that would soon kill the average horse. The camel has to take a drink once in a while, although he can go without it for longer periods than can any other form of wild life. Usually engaged in freighting or farming, his owners need not give much thought to the camel's food supply because he can subsist upon any odd bits of herbage, grasses, weeds, thorny shrubbery, leaves, twigs, and bark. In fact, he

PASSENGER CAMELS COOLING OFF WHILE TOURISTS EXPLORE
THE PYRAMIDS IN EGYPT

Courtesy Chicago Park District

THE TIME-HONORED SHIP OF THE DESERT

Courtesy Chicago Park District

PATIENT AND STRONG, AND ONE OF MAN'S BEST FRIENDS

can find food and nourishment where the horse would starve. In freighting he usually carries a load of about five or six hundred pounds, although there have been quite a few large camels that made good time across the desert with a load of a thousand pounds. The average daily distance traveled is about thirty miles. Without a load, however, and with a fairly lightweight driver, he can trot, gallop, and walk more than one hundred miles a day. Moreover, on this cross-country freighting or messenger work, his splayed, cloven hoofs take him across areas where the horse would sink in to the hocks. In farm work he is used for plowing, harvesting crops, and carrying them to barn or market.

When a year or two old he is trained to kneel, broken to harness, and trained to carry light loads. He easily adapts himself to his new mode of life and is soon one of the burden bearers in the camel caravan. After some experience, the camel becomes amusingly "load wise." He will kneel down and sit quietly while the drivers place the load upon him. When they have finished he sways and moves a bit and thus adjusts himself to the load. If the drivers have piled on too much, however, he flatly refuses to rise to his feet. In other words, it is difficult to overload a camel. In this he displays good sense, for an overloaded horse will at least have a try at a very heavy load even if he injures himself in so doing. Thus it seems that, in this matter of loading, we should talk of "camel sense" rather than "horse sense."

Although noted for their patience and apparent disinterestedness in what is going on about them, camels can become dangerous to man. Although they can do some damage to their drivers or loaders with their great splay feet, their long jaws are much more to be feared. They have a crunching bite that will turn a man's shoulder or arm into a pulp, causing injuries that will keep the man in hospital for months.

When his days of hardship are over, the camel is still good to eat. The meat is fairly nourishing, and the hump is considered quite a delicacy. His long, soft hair is manufactured into cloth that is impervious to water and therefore especially useful for clothing and tents. His hide makes the finest of leather that is used in belts, harness and footwear. Taking everything into considera-

Courtesy Mason Warner, Chicago

CAMEL CARAVAN
The average load for each camel is about five or six hundred pounds of freight. They average about thirty miles per day on cross-country freighting.

tion, it is doubtful if any other animal gives as much of himself to man's general welfare as the humble camel. It is highly probable that he has been closer to man than either the horse or the dog, and was probably the first wild animal to be tamed and put to work for the benefit of mankind.

It should be mentioned here that camels were once given a tryout in the desert country of southwestern United States. When the white man was opening up the southwest, the government was very anxious to aid and assist in developing a freight-wagon trail between points in New Mexico and in southern California. Someone suggested using camels for the exploration work, and thus the first camel caravan in the United States was soon under way. The trip was successful in every way, and the camel was so greatly glorified that it appeared that there should be more of them in this country. A group of New Orleans speculators sent to Egypt for a hundred camels and then sat back to see their fortunes made overnight. The camels arrived, in good condition and ready for work, and some of them were still alive when the first railroads penetrated this new region. The coming of the railroad, of course, prevented further development in the use of camels. Today, of course, he would be outmoded by both railroad and motor truck, as he is in some parts of northern Africa.

In concluding our visit with the camel, it would be well to mention at least one of numerous amusing superstitions concerning this animal. Not so very many years ago it was generally believed that the camel could go many days without drinking water because he carried all the water he needed in his hump and also in one of the four compartments of his digestive organs. Folklore had it that when Arabs were dying of thirst, they would, very reluctantly, kill a camel and save their lives by drinking the water stored in hump and stomach. Needless to say, this was all very ridiculous. But, not knowing any better, millions of people believed it.

STRANGE AFRICAN BIRDS

Side by side with the hyena and jackal, and tearing away at what is left of the lion's latest kill, is the strong-taloned African vulture, the "hyena" of the African birds. He is pretty much the same as the American species in that he is a shockingly foul feeder, especially fond of animal matter in the most advanced stages of decomposition. Equipped with remarkable eyesight, the vulture soars and glides under African skies, seeing everything that happens on the earth below. When the hyenas and jackals suddenly break cover, the vulture is guided to the latest kill, or at least to what is left of it. Down he comes and takes his place alongside the hyena and jackal. Together they clean up the jungle kitchen for their benefactor, the lion.

As the traveler pushes northward toward the Kapiti country he will find a wide variety of birds. Black and white hornbills, guinea fowl, and the francolin, a species of African partridge, are numerous. The bustard, which looks like a grey and brown turkey, does not spend all his days in Africa. The wanderlust gets into his blood at nesting time, and then he flies as far as northern France or England.

Although most of these birds have their peculiarities, none of

Courtesy University of Iowa Museum

AFRICAN HORNBILL FEEDING HIS IMPRISONED MATE

them has such peculiar and interesting habits as the hornbills. They like fruits, but are also fond of carrion, small reptiles, and rodents. Perhaps their most amazing peculiarity is their manner of nesting and raising the young. Selecting a decaying tree that has a suitable hole in the trunk, they will work away on the decaying fiber until the female bird can enter. Once inside, she makes a nest of some of her own feathers and the decayed wood, and settles down to lay eggs. Meanwhile, the male bird flies back and forth with mud and fiber and grass. Then, with the help of the nesting female inside the tree, the male plasters up the hole with clay mixed with gastric secretions until it is just large enough to allow the birds to pass their bills through. Thus the female is imprisoned for from seven to nine weeks, being fed frequently by the male. This food is not in the natural state, for the male first swallows the food which is then enclosed in a bag formed by the lining of the stomach. When he arrives at the opening to the nest, the male regurgitates the food and pokes it through the slit for the female to consume. While being cared for in this manner, the female will lay from two to four eggs. During this long nesting period she usually grows quite fat, in which condition she is considered choice food by the natives. Meanwhile, the hard-worked male grows thinner and thinner and more ragged and bedraggled each day, and by the time the nesting is over he is often more dead than alive. In fact, if a hard cold rain, or a severe change of weather came along just at this particular time in his life, he would probably die from shock.

On the fringes of the Tsavo country are the amazing and numerous weaverbirds. Their nests look like large, old-fashioned beehives in the distance and are hung on acacia trees, which sag under the weight of two or three hundred pendulous nests. These structures are works of art, closely woven and roomy, with the entrance underneath. Sometimes these great weaverbird colonies are stricken helpless and many of them die. At times there is heavy rainfall in this region and the nests, because of their make-up, are filled with water. Should the downpour come during the nesting season, and it sometimes does, every egg and nest is ruined. However, in spite of these occasional tragedies, the species is in little danger of extinction.

Photo by UFA

HERON AND VULTURE PAUSE FOR AN EVENING MEAL ON THE MIGHTY NILE

In the Blue and the White Nile regions, and also along the main streams, there is an amazing abundance of waterfowl, including three varieties of pelicans and many varieties of herons, cranes, spoonbills, storks and flamingoes, swans, geese, ducks and even the handsome teal. Along the fringes of the forests there are beautiful golden orioles, warblers, weaverbirds, while other species dressed in deep blue, scarlet, green, and gold delight the eye as well as the ear. Inland from the streams and lakes we find the graceful golden plover, two or three species of kingfishers, wild pigeons, "crocodile birds" which are related to the plovers, snipe, partridge, grouse, and quail in abundance. And then, overhead, soaring high under the African skies, we find eagles, ospreys, black and white vultures, hawks, owls, and falcons. Truly, the ever-lasting Nile flows through a bird-lover's paradise.

In the Semliki country we see the strange touraco birds. They are related to the cuckoo, and are sometimes called plantain-eaters because of their fondness for that plant. When full grown they measure almost two feet from beak to tail-tip, and apart from the brilliant plumage, the high, fin-shaped crest on their heads gives them a quite distinguished appearance. The bird's cry is much like its name, with the emphasis on the second syllable: "tuuuuurr—AK—ooowww!" This species of touraco is also found in West Africa and usually in the same forests with the well-known African grey parrot, and the whale-headed stork.

The sacred ibis may be seen reposing on one leg on the banks of the Nile. Although found in other parts of Africa, they are, perhaps, more numerous in the middle and lower Nile country. Like the sacred monkeys of India of today, the sacred ibis once lived in the ancient temples of Egypt where they were fed and cared for by the priests. Moreover, in those ancient days, the sacred ibis was embalmed after death with as much care and reverence as were bestowed upon the remains of a prince or high priest. Even to this day, the archaeologists are finding the bones of the sacred ibis in the same tombs and graves as the important Egyptian dignitaries of an earlier day.

Several reasons have been advanced as to why this bird was held in such high regard by the ancient Egyptians. Some worshiped it because they believed that it had made Egypt habitable for man by destroying the numerous venomous and poisonous snakes that had for centuries prevented the settlement of a considerable portion of upper Egypt. Others believed that the silvery white plumage, the black-tipped wings, and the curved bill fitted in quite nicely with certain Egyptian beliefs concerning certain phases of the moon. Since then the sacred ibis has lost most of its ancient prestige and prominence and to most of the modern Egyptians it is just another stork.

The common stork of Europe lives in the same region as the sacred ibis. A winter resident along the Nile, he spends his summers in many parts of Europe. When the month of October rolls around he flies south to Egypt.

THE SECRETARY BIRD

This odd-named, odd-looking, odd-feeding bird of the hawk family has the head and beak of an eagle and the legs of a crane. Its name is derived from the peculiar quill-shaped feathers which tuft out from behind its ears like old-fashioned quills behind the ears of old-fashioned clerks. When the birds are young, their legs are very fragile and snap quite often. But in the older birds they are powerful means of locomotion which send them over the ground at high speed, even when wounded. Although they can fly easily with their long wings, they seem to prefer the ground, and when running they seem to forget that their wings can be used.

Their food is composed mostly of insects, lizards, and snakes. One naturalist reported that he had found lizards, and snakes that measured three feet in length, in a secretary bird's gizzard. Snakes do not bother these strange birds. Leaping on reptiles with their heavy claws, they use their wings as shields to parry the snake's fangs, while kicking their prey to death. When this is difficult, they seize the snake, fly aloft, and drop it from a great height to the ground.

The color of the secretary bird is usually a pearl gray or black. The South African secretary bird, which ranges as far north as Abyssinia, builds its enormous nest in low bushes. It usually has, as a first-floor neighbor, a Cape sparrow which finds the larger nest a fine shield from the sun and wind. The male bird always feeds the female when she is sitting on her eggs. Even after they are hatched, young birds do not try their own feet until five or six months old.

THE OSTRICH

The largest bird in the world, the ostrich is probably also one of the oldest of birds. It is so old that in the millions of years of its existence it has lost the use of its wings, so that now they are merely vestigial remains and serve only to give balance when the bird is in running flight. In addition, it has also lost the first and second toes of its feet, the third toe being very large and padded underneath. In time, like the horse, the ostrich may lose all but the third toe.

Ostriches are to be found in Africa and Arabia. They differ only in that the Arabian ostrich's neck is flesh-colored while its African cousin's is tinted blue. The Somali or African ostrich stands anywhere between six and eight feet in height and weighs about three hundred pounds. On top of its long, snake-like neck are a flattened head and a short beak. The male's feathers are usually black while the wings and the tail are white. It is these tail-plumes that have made the ostrich a highly desirable bird to catch, for they are white, beautifully curled, and were much sought after for feminine decorative purposes. Catching an ostrich is not an easy job. It is very keensighted, wary and fleet of foot, and can lead a hunter around in circles indefinitely. A Somali native hides in an ostrich's nest, which is simply a hole in the sand, after he has done away with the eggs. When the ostrich approaches and finds the native, it is surprised long enough for him to shoot the bird with a poisoned arrow.

At present, though, the ostrich has been domesticated, so that fear of its extinction has been allayed. A number of ostrich farms are to be found in Australia and California, and they are furnishing enough ostrich feathers for the trade. In some sections, ostriches have been trained as beasts of burden.

A peculiarity of the ostrich is its mincing walk, not to be expected from such a long-legged, ungainly bird. In addition it is addicted to what is known as the "waltz" and the "roll." Particularly is this noticeable in male ostriches when they are courting. While running they will stop suddenly and, with wings raised, whirl around and around until they stop from exhaustion.

At times an entire herd becomes subject to this frenetic seizure and a view of them is startling. When "rolling," male ostriches fall to their knees, flap their wings, extend their necks and fluff their tail feathers into a fan. In this condition, their eyesight becomes impaired and they can be approached by hunters, who wring their necks. Otherwise, the male ostrich is quite a fighter; and when he is defending his nest of fifteen three-pound eggs or fighting for a mate, he uses his powerful, club-tipped legs to good advantage.

Photo by UFA

AFRICAN OSTRICH

When in danger he does not hide his head in the sand. He merely spreads himself flat upon the ground until danger is past.

Black Star photo by William Fox

CLOSE-UP OF THE INDIAN KING COBRA

ANIMAL LIFE OF INDIA

DISTRIBUTION OF INDIAN MAMMALS

INDIA'S three geographical divisions are so varied that a wide range of animal, bird, fish, reptile, and insect life is to be found in its confines. Its main southern peninsula, for instance, is tropical in climate; therefore, its vegetation is similarly tropical and its animal life is the kind that is usually found in the hot countries. Here, the black leopard pads its way secretively through bamboo forests and dense thickets. Mango groves abound together with bushes and shrubs of the thorny variety in which the cheetah stalks the graceful antelope.

Another geographical division takes in the territory of the Indus and the sacred river Ganges. Here, the topography is flat, in the main, with scant vegetation, especially in the Indus plain region. Few trees grow and those, like most desert vegetation, are stunted. Thorny shrubs and underbrush are to be found, with occasional clumps of palm trees and bamboo forests. The Ganges River district, extending as far south as the Bay of Bengal, includes the low countries such as Orissa and the rolling foothills of the Himalayas. Dense evergreen forests are to be found here together with many other varieties of vegetation which thrive in the rainy climate. In the dank swamps and in the *tarais* of the foothills, the Indian tiger finds its safest refuge, hunting antelopes, deer, and wild hogs. It is to this section that the tiger-hunting expeditions go, shooting the beasts from rickety perches atop of lumbering elephants. The sloth bear, too, hunts its ants, fruit, and honey in the hills and forests. Large elephant herds crash through the jungles of Orissa and trumpet madly in the hills that usher in the heights of the Himalayas. Most of them, however, are to be found in the northeast from Assam to Burma.

The third geographical division of India includes the highlands of the Himalayas, which run straight through the country. The southwestern Himalayas grow tropical trees and shrubs as well as the pines and oaks of the colder countries. The eastern Himalayan section is likewise tropical with its rhododendron, orchidaceous and magnolia growths. In the summer, the Himalayan bear prefers to remain in the upper regions; but when the snow falls and the cold weather comes on, it descends into the valleys. The chamois, the ibex, wild sheep, and goats frequent these higher lands stepping surefootedly from crag to crag. Here, too, the eagle builds its eyrie and swoops down to pick off a juicy wild pig or a lamb.

In spite of its many tropical sections, India's birds are not as colorful as they are in most of the hot countries. Its salt-water snakes are poisonous and are feared by the natives. In the rainy season India's gardens are wriggly with serpents both deadly and non-poisonous. Tigers are to be found in most of the sections of the country although leopards are more common. All in all, though, India's fauna is interesting and the many animals to be found only in India have always proved highly diverting to naturalists.

THE ROYAL BENGAL TIGER

The Royal Bengal tiger is a ferocious savage beast, and in its native Indian haunts, the long, sleek cat is a beautiful, muscular animal. From tail to tip of nose a full grown male will average nine to twelve feet and stand three to three and one-fourth feet high at the shoulder. Females average slightly less in length and height. The coloration of the tiger does not differ greatly. Its cross stripes on the tawny yellow coat may furnish protective coloring in the reed haunts. Accentuating the beauty of the coat and further disguising the animal are the white shadings varied with vertical black stripes or elongated ovals. These white markings are best defined on the face and posterior surface of the ears.

INDIAN TIGERS—MALE, FEMALE, AND CUB

These specimens were taken in Nepal.

Courtesy Chicago Park District

TWENTY-EIGHT-YEAR-OLD "RAJAH" BENGAL TIGER
His minimum per diem food allowance is twelve pounds of fresh beef.

Zoo tigers as a whole are poor representatives of this powerful cat family. Deprived of his natural haunts, his vigorous nightly travels and the ensuing mortal struggles with other large animals, the poor captive in the metropolitan zoo soon becomes a spiritless, lanky, bony creature more dead than alive. His bulky broad shoulders fade away, and his well developed back and loins become mere shadows of what were once fine hard muscles.

Having an extraordinary equipment of teeth and claws, and powerful muscles to use them, the tiger is the most dangerous of the cat family. Numerous stories have been told of how with one deadly stroke an enraged tiger has torn an arm from the shoulder of a native, leaving the bleeding, shredded member hanging by only a piece of skin.

Rarely, however, will a tiger attack an armed man unless provoked. Its tremendous strength is usually exerted on other wild animals in its nightly prowls through the jungles. Particularly stealthy in more populous sections, the tiger is said to eat only a part of its victim it kills by daylight. It will return after dusk, if at all, to finish the feast.

Unlike the jungle tigers, those found in the hills—high up in the Himalayas—at certain seasons will stalk their game by day as well as night, probably less mindful of traps because of their more barren and desolate habitat.

The tiger is a true native of Asia and exists naturally nowhere else in the world today. Not to our knowledge has it ever existed outside of captivity anywhere but in Asia. Growing larger to the north of India, the Chinese and Siberian tigers are definitely huskier, bigger animals than the Indian group. The largest Indian tiger-skin known is from an animal killed by the Maharaja of Cuch Behar—eleven feet and seven inches in length.

Courtesy Chicago Park District

THE HANDSOME SIBERIAN TIGER
Note the powerful and muscular front paws.

True cats, tigers retract their claws into sheaths, causing their footsteps to be absolutely noiseless as they creep up on their prey. Tigers are flesh eaters and, like other members of the cat family, destroy living animals.

Only in those parts of India where the European has entered and taken hold has the tiger menace to cattle and domestic animals been abated. The Indian peasant, even in the populous native sections, is helpless against the ferocious onslaught on his cattle. And in the jungle and on islands at river mouths, the tigers, where they exist, hold full sway.

Actually, in many parts of India these once plentiful animals are now scarce. Only on the preserves of the powerful rajahs and on the estates of the great potentates do they abound in really large numbers. Here it is said the deer and pigs are so numerous that tigers are welcome to keep their number down. The Sunderbunds, the unwholesome isles at the mouth of the Ganges, still swarm with tigers. Likewise the Malay peninsula supports many of this fierce tribe.

Famous among story-tellers as a man-eater, the tiger actually does not become such until driven to desperation by extreme hunger, old age, or sickness. Out of the running, the old tiger begins to draw in on populated districts. The smell of food brings him closer and closer. Finally, almost mad with hunger, he grabs a sheep or dog or even a defenseless woman or child, and seeks his lair in the dense trackless bush. Once having tasted this flesh, the tiger is indeed a great menace to the community and must be stalked until he is found and killed, for his taste becomes set more strongly with each new victim.

Natives use pitfalls, traps, spring guns, and poison arrows to hunt the tiger. Best known, however, is the game of sportsmen who shoot the tigers from the backs of elephants as they are driven from their lairs by the natives, who beat the bush with sticks. Many young tigers are captured, tamed, and taken into captivity by this method, although the majority are trapped.

THE BLACK LEOPARD OF
  INDIA AND ASIA

Courtesy Chicago Park District

LEOPARDS OF INDIA

Also one of the forty-odd species of the famous cat family, the leopard is smaller in size than the tiger, but considerably more ferocious. Living mainly in trees or caves and coming forth almost exclusively at night, the leopard is seen less by humans than many rarer animals in the same districts.

The largest of these Indian leopards are known as panthers. Immensely strong, though really not so formidable in appearance, they are well known everywhere as cattle, sheep, and dog thieves. Their favorite method of killing is to seize the prey by the throat, and cling with the claws until the spine is broken or the victim is strangled. Treacherous in the extreme, the leopard and his spots have come to stand for all that is cowardly and untrustworthy among mankind.

Like tigers, panthers sometimes become man-eaters, first as a last resort against starvation, and finally because a strong taste has been developed for human flesh. Because they frequently feed on putrid flesh, the wounds of a leopard often inflict blood poisoning on an injured victim. Natives shy in terror from this deadly, treacherous cat. Never to be trusted, they say, he is much more to be feared than either the lion or tiger, who attack man usually only when provoked to rage.

Courtesy Chicago Park District

CLOSE-UP OF BLACK LEOPARD OF
LINCOLN PARK ZOO, CHICAGO

The mother leopard usually has four or five kittens in a litter, and white men have found the furry, soft little creatures to make very amusing pets, and in spite of the terrified warnings of the natives, have continued in their attempts to tame the cubs. A story is told of an English merchant in Hong Kong, who raised a leopard from a young kitten as a house pet. Very fond of his animal and overly proud of it, he ordered it brought to the dining room while he was entertaining a party of guests. One of the women in the party was so disturbed at the sight of the long sleek creature and its narrowed eyes that it was felt best to take it away at once. But the smell of food attracted the animal. It refused to budge when the coolie pulled on its leash. Suddenly the leopard sprang on the defenseless servant with whom it had been on the "best of terms" for years, and seized him by the throat. He fell dying, with his throat in bloody, ragged shreds before horror stricken dinner guests a moment later.

Black Star photo by William Fox

THE BEAUTIFUL "OUNCE" OR SNOW LEOPARD OF INDIA AND ASIA

High in the mountain ranges of India are found the beautiful snow leopards. Paler in color than the panthers, these animals have thick, soft, woolly coats and long tails. They have been said to resemble angora cats in the coloring and texture of their coats and in their smoky-blue eyes.

Living on wild sheep, ibex, and other mountain animals, they are rarely seen by humans. Sportsmen in search of this animal have found him difficult to stalk because of his ability to climb trees, and his strong, protective coloring. Once taken into captivity, however, the snow leopard has proved to be the tamest and gentlest of all caged carnivora.

CHEETAH

Known as the "hunting leopard" because of the ease with which it can be used for this sport, the cheetah resembles more closely a dog than any of the rest of the cat family. Somewhat smaller than leopards, the animal stands high on its legs, has a short rounded head, and claws which, unlike those of other cats, cannot be retracted into hornlike sheaths. Its fur is short and woolly, and its chief distinguishing marks are small, solid black spots instead of rosettes or circles on the coat.

Courtesy Field Museum of Natural History
THE CHEETAH OR HUNTING LEOPARD OF INDIA AND ASIA
Although the cheetah is a member of the cat family, he has feet like the dog, with non-retractile claws.

First used by native princes for taking antelope and deer, the cheetah was discovered to be ideal as a hunting animal. Interestingly, cheetahs cannot be caught and tamed before they have developed naturally those characteristics which will enable them to excel in the chase. Man has not been able to instill the qualities of the hunting dog in the young animal. That is still left to the mysteries of its bringing up among its own kind.

Once caught, the cheetah takes about six months of taming before it is docile, but afterward will even sleep in the same bed with its master. Interesting stories are told of this taming process. A combination starving and bullying of the animal is managed by tying it to the foot of a bed, lashing the bed posts and floor with a whip, introducing a continual pandemonium of human and other noises, and feeding the poor beast just enough to keep it alive. Occasionally taken for a walk, tightly leashed to four or five natives, the cowering animal is led through dense crowds and as much uproar in city streets as possible. The object, of course, is to inject fear of man into the proud young animal.

Once tamed, the cheetah is blindfolded and taken into the country. Released for the chase, it is permitted to see the game only after getting close by! The cheetah is a remarkably fast runner and can corner the fastest deer. When he is successful, and the hunt is over, the victorious Indian "hunting leopard" is given a full drink of his victim's warm blood as his reward for the chase.

ELEPHANTS

Mightiest of all four-footed animals today are the two remaining species of elephants, the Asiatic and the African. These gentle powerful beasts are effective reminders of the giant mammals that once roamed over the earth in great numbers. Their strange appearance, tremendous strength, endurance, and capacity to learn have resulted in their almost universal use by man for both entertainment and labor.

A sharp difference can be noted between the Asiatic or Indian and the African species of elephants, the most obvious of these being that in almost every respect the Indian is the smaller of the two types. While the African animal often stands more than eleven feet at the shoulder, the Indian rarely exceeds ten feet.

The ears of the African may be as much as five feet across, but the Indian's ears are little more than one half of that width. Both sexes have long, well-developed tusks in the African species, while the tusks are smaller and lighter in the male and scarcely noticeable, if present at all, in the female of the Indian species.

Other prominent differences are the arched back of the Indian as contrasted to the hollowed back of the African animals, likewise the lighter, smoother skin in the former.

Courtesy Chicago Park District

INDIAN OR ASIATIC ELEPHANT

One exceedingly interesting difference in the two types is the fact that, while the Indian elephant lies down to rest or to sleep, the African animal never gets off his feet except to roll on the ground and scratch

Courtesy Mason Warner, Chicago

ASIATIC ELEPHANT AND HIS MAHOUT

Black Star photo

INDIAN COW ELEPHANT AND HER YOUNG CALF
Note the small ears, a physical feature that distinguishes the Asiatic
from the African species.

his back; he is said to stand sleeping unprotected by any shade in the hottest tropical sun. Recalling those elephants watched in circuses, most of us will remember that they are commonly seen in a lying or sitting position. Circuses and side shows use Indian elephants almost exclusively.

In disposition the elephant is gentle, almost timid. It has only one pace, a slow loping walk, which can be sped up to a fast shuffle of about fifteen miles per hour on occasion. Usually silent, the elephant may make a series of short, blowing sounds when charging, although the Indian elephant may remain silent even when provoked to a rage.

As practically every circus-lover knows, the elephant's trunk, in the upper part of which are his tremendously keen nostrils, is almost as effective as human hands. For tearing huge trees out of the ground, roots and all, in his jungle home, or for picking up a single peanut on the floor of his cage under the "big tent" the elephant uses his long, waving trunk with more dexterity than seems possible.

His sight being very poor, however, and his hearing not much better in spite of the big, fanlike ears, the elephant is compensated with a powerful sense of smell, probably the best in all the animal kingdom. A man can be detected several miles away, and greeted or avoided, as the animal chooses. Slow and sure in movement, bulky and powerful in strength, equipped with a memory to which natives and European trainers alike testify, the elephant has been of great service to man for many centuries.

For these reasons, and because the elephant is easily fed, existing mostly on leaves, grass, bamboo shoots, and fruits in his natural habitat, man has always found it extremely easy and profitable to domesticate the huge, ungainly, but willing beast.

Once the Asiatic rulers used their big bulls as an indication of power in warfare. Orientals soon learned the value of the elephant as a show animal in the royal parades before the populace. For ages the beasts have been of invaluable aid in moving and stacking heavy timber, in dragging weighty loads through water and mud, and over rough, almost impassable surfaces. More recently the Western world has developed the circus elephant, which does "stunts," clowns in fancy costumes, and meekly accepts its share of the heavy labor of moving-day in the circus. Modern sportsmen, particularly the English, have made great use of the beast for tiger hunting. Protected by its bulk and their own great distance from the ground, they shoot the prey from a vantage point not to be obtained by any other hunting aid.

Since elephants have been kept in captivity in India for as long as one hundred and thirty years, it probably is not assuming too much to reckon that they may live to one hundred and fifty years in their wild state, although, of course, their exact life expectancy can scarcely be measured. Females usually bear only one calf at a time, the period of gestation being eighteen to twenty-two months. The young elephant does not mature until about thirty years old. Although the animals usually travel in herds from half a dozen to hundreds in number when foraging for food, the old bulls live as individuals most of the year. Some of them, with

Black Star photo
INDIAN BUFFALO AND CALF

one or both tusks broken off or missing altogether, bear the marks in their leathery hides of many a fierce encounter in the jungle forest.

THE WATER BUFFALO—A DOMESTICATED GIANT

The most common of the domesticated buffaloes seen in India is the variety used in rice culture, and commonly referred to as "water buffalo." It is a native of the East Indies, but domesticated in India, it has thrived so well that from there it has been introduced into Egypt, Greece, Italy, Hungary, and other parts of Europe.

This animal has beautifully twisted horns, thick, and broad at the base, rough up to the middle, somewhat triangular in section. The horns, directed backward, lie on the shoulders when the animal walks or runs, with its muzzle projecting characteristically forward. The hair is short and scanty, almost bristly, slightly longer on head, shoulders, and front of neck, and all but black in color. The bare, brown, polished hide is, however, the more striking feature. The animal measures about seven feet in length, and stands about four feet high at the shoulder.

There is a variety of this buffalo, native to India, known as the arnee; it is larger than the more common animal. The head of one has been known to have measured thirteen feet six inches along the horns. It is found in the Indian islands and in farther India in a wild state, but it is also domesticated and used as a beast of burden.

Even the smaller water buffalo is larger and much more powerful than the ox, and capable of dragging or carrying a far heavier load. The slow-moving buffalo used as a draft animal on the farm is less docile than the ox, but it is possible for a master to win its complete confidence. Strangers, however, are unsafe, and in their presence the buffalo may become dangerous and destructive. Most valuable as a servant in the cultivation of rice, the buffalo is able to wade through mud up to his thighs, and must be permitted to wallow and bathe in water every day. He seems to be happiest when lying in water with only the nostrils protruding above the surface.

The female yields a much greater quantity of milk than most dairy cattle, and it is of excellent quality, nourishing, but of peculiar flavor. It is from buffalo milk that the ghee, or semifluid butter, of India is made. The buffalo's hide is greatly valued for its strength and durability, but its flesh is decidedly inferior to that of the ox.

In the wild state, the buffalo is one of the most feared of the jungle animals. No animal which he might meet on the jungle trails is too large or too fearsome to frighten him, and the male is a match for even the tiger.

Haunting swampy marshes, where he may satisfy his love of wallowing in the mud and water, the buffalo is usually found in herds of up to a hundred head. These herds keep together during the greater part of the year; but at the beginning of the rutting season each male will lead three or four cows away from the herd and off by themselves.

RHINOCEROSES

Strange is the sight in the cool Indian evening of a mother rhinoceros with her calf startled by some strange noise or queer odor. Along the bank of a river the pair runs, with the young one in front and, seemingly attached, the mother behind. Though the pace may quicken, the same close relationship persists. It is believed that the mother guides the calf with her single horn against the young one's rump. To add to the confusion and strangeness, a number of birds fly over their heads, emitting noisy cries. These, known as rhinoceros birds, stay close to the huge beast and its young and seem to warn them of danger.

Related to the hippopotamus, tapir, and elephant, the Indian rhinoceros is one of three species found in Asia. Africa is the only other continent in which this animal can be found, although there formerly was an American species, now extinct. It is huge (the second largest mammal now living on land), and is an unprepossessing-looking animal. Its low intelligence seems to be mirrored in its physical aspect. The rhinoceros stands about five and a half feet high. Its thick, heavy, hairless skin hangs in drooping folds, dividing the body of the animal into what seems to be several sections. On its head are two erect, pricked-up ears, giving the animal an acute sense of hearing. The small, lackluster eyes are poor and serve the beast but little. The Indian species, like that of Malay, has a single horn at the end of its nose. Other species have two horns. Its olfactory sense, like its hearing, is acute.

A herbivorous animal, the rhinoceros lives on leaves, grass and other vegetation. During the daylight hours, the animal sleeps, usually awakening in the cool of the evening. After eating he enters muddy water or watery mud to wallow and bathe. In these somewhat limited activities he engages during many of his waking hours.

Like many other animals he surprises man with the speed with which he can carry his heavy body. Ordinarily lazy and slow-moving, he at times will break into a trot and, if pressed, will even gallop. However, a horse can outrun the rhinoceros, and this fact, together with the animal's normal timidity and herbivorous appetite, keeps him from being a fearsome animal to man.

Black Star photo

THE INDIAN RHINOCEROS

Pauls Photos, Chicago

THE INDIAN RHINOCEROS
With all that thick "armor plate" it is easy
to understand that the Indian rhinoceros has
few, if any, enemies.

Courtesy American Museum of Natural History

THE SOUTH AMERICAN COUSIN OF THE INDIAN AND MALAYAN TAPIR

TAPIR

An odd-looking animal, related on the one hand to the rhinoceros and on the other to the horse, the tapir has changed practically not at all through long ages. Probably the most shy and inoffensive of all animals in Indo-Malaysia is this odd piglike creature.

Venturing from the deep forests and water holes only at night, the tapir exists on the plants and berries it finds in its wanderings. Like the pig, which it resembles, the tapir wallows in the mud, probably to coat its back with a protection against bites of flies and other insects.

Harmless in the extreme, the tapir will run even from dogs, and almost never defends itself. Uttering a shrill cry when aroused, however, the female will attack an enemy molesting her young. Natives have several methods of hunting these animals, which are sometimes eaten, and whose thick hides are cut into thongs for reins and bridles. The lasso is a favorite method, but very difficult to use in heavy forests where the tapir makes its home.

Most deadly foe of the tough little tapir, which stands scarcely over three feet high, is the tiger, although the latter's attack is by no means always fatal. Many hundreds of tapirs are said to bear deep, ugly scars in their almost horny backs, indicating the terrible gashes made by the claws of an attacking tiger. The tiger, falling on the animal from behind with intent to crush its neck, was unable to get a good hold and succeeded only in gashing the tapir as it made its getaway.

The distribution of tapirs has presented an interesting problem to students of animal geography. In addition to the one Malay species there are four South American species. The wide intervening area is accounted for by the fact that tapir fossils have been found in both China and the area that is now the United States. Strangely, these fossils show that, unlike the horse—one of its relatives—the tapir has scarcely changed in the hundreds of centuries gone by since the Stone Age.

Sportsmen report that the tapir is easily tamed, especially the young, and could be domesticated in a few generations.

SACRED MONKEYS OF THE HINDUS

Believed by the Hindus to be the reincarnation of some revered person, the entellus monkey is treated as a deity and given all the reverence and protection due a god. Rusty brown in color and about two feet in length, this monkey has a tail almost three feet long. As it sits on limbs with filled cheek pouches, tail hanging straight down, it appears to be a grave, dignified, serious fellow; but when disturbed it shouts, cries, and creates a hub-bub. The monkeys become especially lively and vicious when they encounter a python, their most dreaded enemy. At times, a number of these monkeys will swarm down upon a ten-foot python and bite and tear it to pieces.

Not only is it considered unforgivable in India to annoy, injure, or tease one of these deified monkeys, but the priests of the temples in India feed them and give them every conceivable

Courtesy American Museum of Natural History

NILGIRI LANGUR MONKEYS OF INDIA

kind of protection. As a result they multiply rapidly. As many
as four hundred have been seen in one tribe. Having learned
that they will be fed by the priests, they make a continuous round
of the temples, sometimes traveling long distances. Whenever
food becomes scarce at the settlements and religious men have
nothing to hand out, the monkeys move out to the nearby agricultural regions where they cause enormous damage to fruit and
grain crops undisturbed.

Living up to twenty years, they become very infirm in old
age. At the same time they get morose, disagreeable, and vicious.
Often an aged monkey will start a free-for-all, and since the
monkey members of his tribe are not Hindus and do not hold
him sacred, he is frequently torn to pieces by them.

"RHESUS MONKEY"

Found in northern India and widely used for all kinds of
laboratory experiments is the "Rhesus monkey," as it is known
to laboratory scientists. Properly, this species is known as the
Bengal macaque, though called the Bandarlog by Kipling in his
Jungle Books.

Courtesy Chicago Park District

THE RHESUS MONKEY OF INDIA
Note the stoutly-built forearm, and the
almost human hand.

Courtesy Chicago Park District

GOLDEN OR RHESUS MONKEY OF
INDIA WITH FOUR-MONTHS-OLD
BABY

The Rhesus monkey belongs to what is known as the Old World type, having close-set nostrils and cheek pouches. Usually about two feet long, with a tail approximately one foot in length, this animal has a strong robust body and short but powerful legs. Its prominent facial characteristics—thick, protruding lips, heavy ridges above eyes, projecting muzzle, and decided cheek pouches —give this monkey a distinctive face. In color the animal is usually a yellowish gray, with a short, hairy coat.

Like other macaques, both sexes travel together in large groups. Emotional, as are all primates, the macaques have been discovered to express their feelings by a series of distinctive sounds varying from guttural monotones of displeasure to harsh shrieks of fright or warning. Whining entreaties, growling responses, and grunting chuckles, are some of the varieties of response catalogued by scientists studying this species.

Although young macaques are kittenish and very docile, tempting as playthings to anyone who sees them, the more mature animal has an ugly disposition in captivity. Nervousness and extreme irritability characterize the reactions of the caged adult. Keepers of zoos report many painful bites as a result of their contacts with the macaques.

Scientists have been particularly interested in these animals since it has been discovered that they harbor "human" parasites in great quantities. Used for experimental studies of these parasites, the macaque is valued considerably as a laboratory specimen by research men.

Macaques spend much of their time, as do all primates, cleaning themselves and one another, and eating. Their cheek pouches are used to store bits of fruit, insects, seeds, and other food which can be chewed up and swallowed at a later and more leisurely hour. Like the groups caged in metropolitan zoos, the wild monkeys cling to one another and care for one another as if in strong need of protection. Their almost pathetic need of the group is quite general in all conditions and species.

THE GIBBON OF INDIA

The first time man saw a gibbon in the forests of India, he probably could hardly believe his eyes. Here was a monkey-like creature, without a tail, and walking erect as does a man! The gibbon even walks without touching the ground with his hands or arms, as do the gorilla and orangutan. Instead, his ex-tremely long arms and elon-gated hands swing loosely along as do the arms of a walking man.

Courtesy American Museum of Natural History
INDIAN FEMALE GIBBON
AND BABY

A primitive ape, black, grey, or brown in coloring, the gibbon is usually slender and stands only about thirty inches tall. Its body, covered with soft, wooly fur, is topped by a small, round head. The gibbons are inhabitants of the forests of India, their long arms enabling them to swing themselves from bough to bough with extreme agility. In this way they are able to cover great distances through the trees.

Eating fruit, leaves, all sorts of insects, and even small birds, up to a hundred travel together in troops at night uttering loud cries and calls. During the day they usually remain quiet.

In captivity they are usually gentle and even affectionate, but at times show a temper. Under the restraints of a zoo, they do not live long and seldom reproduce while in captivity.

ANTELOPES AND DEER

The number of species of antelopes in India is small when com-pared with the number in Africa. However, this country among its several species has the true antelope and the blackbuck, which was first named antelope, and from which the other members of the genus get their general name. Antelopes closely resemble deer in general appearance, but differ essentially from them.

THE SAIGA ANTELOPE OF ASIA
(See page 171)

Antelope horns, for example, unlike those of the deer, are not deciduous, but are permanent; are never branched, but are often twisted spirally, and may be borne by both sexes. The antelope is included in the family of hollow-horned ruminants, of which sheep and oxen are members.

The blackbuck of India gets its name from the color of the male, whose coat is of a deep, brown-black coloring. Its belly is white. Its horns are spiral in shape, usually having three or four turns and reaching a length of thirty inches, if the cork-screw were to be unwound. The female is without horns and is light fawn in coloring. Herds composed of as many as fifty does and a single buck are found in the salt plains and also along the coastline of Guserat and east into Orissa. This antelope is hunted by sportsmen, and its flesh, though dry and unsavory, is eaten by the Hindus, who refuse to eat the flesh of a second species of antelope found in India. These, known as blue-cows because of the bluish coloring of the male, are mistakenly believed to be members of the cow family and hence are held sacred.

The gazelle is another member of the antelope family found in India. Of medium size, seldom over thirty inches tall, it is sandy-colored with white stripes on each side of its face. Most of the females, like all the males, have ringed horns which curve slightly forward. As though equipped for kneeling in prayer, the gazelle has tufts of hair on its knees.

One Indian antelope, or rather, a group of several species, has four horns. The two real horns are smooth, erect and about three inches long. The other two are solid, short, and blunted. These are seldom more than an inch in length. These four-horned antelopes are usually found in pairs and are fairly numerous. Like most of the antelopes, they are very timid and shy.

The deer suffers from the attacks of the tiger as much as does the antelope. Several species of deer are found in India, including some that stand five feet tall and some with a three-foot antler spread. The most common and interesting species are the twelve point (so called because of the number of projections of the antlers); the spotted deer; the samohar, the axis; the barking deer, which has tusks; the mouse deer; and the musk deer, which is found mostly in Tibet.

YAK

The wild and the domesticated yak, found in the mountainous regions of Tibet and the border regions of India, is a species of ox and is closely related to the bison. It is one of the largest oxen found. In a wild state the yak stands six feet at the shoulder and has a black coat. When domesticated the animal is usually smaller and a mixture of white appears in the coat.

The body of the animal is covered with a thick, shaggy coat of long, silky hair hanging down like the fleece of a sheep, completely covering the tail and forming a lengthy fringe along the

Courtesy Chicago Park District

INDIAN YAK: A MOST USEFUL
ANIMAL

Courtesy Chicago Park District

INDIAN YAK BEGINNING TO SHED
HIS HEAVY WINTER COAT

shoulders, flanks, and thighs, much like the hair of a well-groomed Scotch terrier. This fringe was apparently developed as a protection to the animal in its mountainous haunts, as the long hair forms a sort of mat which defends the body from the effects of the cold when the animal is resting in the snow.

The yak has two heavy, hollow, black horns which, growing from the side of the head, curve upward and slightly forward. These animals are great travelers while in a wild state and cover wide areas during the course of a year. At the end of the yak's tail is a tuft of fine hair which is used as a fly-whisk by Indian princes.

The traveler from central India to Ladek, near the northern border, comes in close contact with the domesticated variety. When the mountains are reached, the traveler is given a yak to ride. Uncomfortable and frightening though this may be to the passenger, he usually casts aside his fear and mounts the ungainly beast. The only alternative is to walk; there is no other means of transportation.

The natives of Tibet have many other uses for this animal. He is of great importance to them. The yak is employed as a beast of burden, but never for tillage or draught; the milk is very rich and yields excellent butter; the flesh is of the finest quality, and that of the calves far superior to ordinary veal. The hair is spun into ropes and the hide is made into coverings for tents. The soft hair from the slight hump and withers is woven into a fine, strong cloth.

IBEX

The Asiatic species of the wild goat, the ibex, is the finest of all those known. Roaming through the highest of Asia's mountain ranges, the ibex fears only the snow leopard and the wild dog, its two natural enemies. The broad strong horns are the chief characteristic of the ibex found in the Himalayas. These have been known to exceed fifty-four inches, measuring along the curve.

Strange tales are told of the agility and almost miraculous surefootedness of these mountain goats, which have been seen to spring from perpendicular heights of forty feet, and to de-

THE MARKHOR,
OFTEN REFERRED
TO AS KING OF
ALL WILD GOATS

The Markhor is found
in Northwestern India.
Extremely agile, the
animal can climb
around in his mountain
home with the assur-
ance of a monkey
climbing a tree.

Black Star photo

scend a "chimney" in a mountain face by zigzagging from side
to side down its steep incline.

Interesting is the fact that the young can be tamed, but scarcely confined. Given large grounds to roam and a variety of background, the kid will spring to the roof of the house and remain
there all day in a spot—often precarious—of his own choosing.

It has been suggested often that the ibex be domesticated. But
the advantages offered are not sufficient to overcome the difficulty
in confining it, once it is tamed.

ASIATIC BEARS

Commonest of the bears in India and one of the most interesting species, is the small, ugly sloth bear. Like the other bear

Photo by UFA

THE THREE-TOED SLOTH

Except when feeding, this strange creature spends most of his life hanging to a tree as shown above. He is unusually muscular and when he once takes hold with his long, sharp and powerful claws it is extremely difficult to dislodge him. Explorers and hunters give him a wide berth.

types, with his short, bulky body, he appears to have had a dog ancestor and to have passed through many modifying stages since. Averaging only two to three hundred pounds in weight, the little sloth bear sits and stands, as do other bears, on his haunches, and runs at a rolling loping pace.

Unlike other bears he is equipped with long, curved claws, which, together with his strong skull and jaws, enable him to attack hard, rocky soil as effectively as a pickaxe in the hands of a husky man. The dirt flies in all directions at once. With his funnel-like lips, the sloth bear sucks up grubs, ants, and other insects from the spot where he has dug into the earth.

From infancy the sloth bear's muscular power and sharp, curved claws are of great aid to him. A basket test made with some six-weeks-old cubs was interesting. The cubs were put into the basket which was then turned upside down. Even with shaking, the hold of the tenacious little cubs could not be loosened. Imagine then, the effect on a human, when attacked by the fully-developed adult sloth bear on the warpath! Arms and legs have been torn almost to ribbons in such encounters.

The Indian bear found in the Himalayas is much like the European black bear in appearance and habits. Distinguished by the white half-moon on his throat, this bear like most others lives entirely on fruits, vegetables, and the sap from small shoots.

Small, smooth-coated, with a yellow patch on his throat resembling a mustard plaster, the little sun bear is the most comical of all the bear tribe. He prefers honey to all other foods, and in his natural state, exists almost entirely on that sweet food. In captivity any sweet stuff will do. Often he is referred to as the honey bear.

About four feet high, accustomed to walking upright to a greater extent than most bear types, the sun bear is easy to tame. He makes an excellent zoo resident because of his queer and amusing antics. The Malay Peninsula has furnished many of these bears and their cubs to zoos all over the world.

JACKAL

Haunting the outskirts of Indian cities is a tribe of wild dogs known as jackals, second in importance and number only to wolves. At night the hungry packs make disturbing outcries, and many are the stories of the panic-stricken natives who never grow used to the sound.

Jackals live largely on refuse. They kill food only when they find wounded and crippled animals in their path. Not so big nor so strong as wolves, they likewise lack the courage to attack and kill their own prey.

White men in India have found a use for these little animals by hunting them in lieu of foxes. Not so fast as the fox nor yet so courageous when cornered, nevertheless they show a remarkable amount of endurance in the chase and usually keep well ahead of the hounds for at least three or four miles.

The young are easily tamed, developing and reacting to their surroundings much as do house dogs. Interesting and entertaining as pets, these pups eat fruits and vegetables eagerly. Rudyard Kipling is responsible for the popularization of the jackal in adventure and fiction stories. The American coyote is probably its nearest relative in habits and description.

WILD DOGS

Kipling's descriptions of the "dhole" or wild red dog of Indian jungles are known to nearly all his readers. Larger than jackals and much fiercer, they roam hills and jungles, although their favorite haunts are the uplands of the Indian Ghats. Like the jackals and others of their kind, the "dholes" hunt in packs.

Natives, and often white men, tell stories of these fierce little animals taking prey right out of the mouths of tigers. It is from the "dholes" undoubtedly that tigers have learned to fear dogs generally. Often tigers have been known to take to trees in their attempt to escape a desperate "dhole."

MONGOOSE

Exterminator of snakes, rats, mice, and other vermin, the weasel-like mongoose of India is smaller than its Egyptian cousin and measures from fifteen to eighteen inches, with a bushy tail about as long again. Its fur is brownish- to yellowish-grey and the hair is tough, stiff, long, and white-ringed. Its sharp teeth indicate that it is a carnivorous animal, and its favorite foods are rats and mice, and the eggs, young, and even the adults of various reptile species.

It shows no fear in the presence of huge Indian snakes, attacking its prey eagerly. It is not immune to the venom of poisonous snakes, however, and when wounded usually suffers death as frequently as other victims of such snakes. However, its quickness and agility make it a most difficult target for the snake, and the thick skin and heavy, bristly hair which becomes erect under excitement make it difficult for the reptile to inflict a wound. In the meantime, the strong, sharp teeth of the mongoose crush the skull of the snake. After killing the reptile, the mongoose eats it with great gusto.

Black Star photo by William Fox

THE COURAGEOUS INDIAN MONGOOSE

Although not immune to the cobra's poisonous bite, the mongoose will fight any and
all cobras that cross his trail. He is usually the victor, finishing the fight by sinking his
sharp fangs into the cobra's head.

Black Star photo by William Fox

THE KING COBRA OF INDIA

Recent reports from India state that the deadly venom of the cobra causes more than 20,000 deaths every year. All people bitten do not die, however. If the bite is not soon followed by fatal results the indications are that the cobra's poison glands were exhausted when he struck.

Because the plantations of Jamaica were rat-infested, mongooses were carried half way around the world to that island. Crop losses caused by rats were reduced a half million dollars and the island was practically freed of the rodents. However, that meant the mongoose had to find other food sources. It turned to birds, small game, and poultry. Now the mongoose itself is considered a pest in Jamaica.

COBRAS

More than fifty varieties of snakes exist in India and surrounding regions, and of these about one-third are poisonous. One of the most feared snakes in the world is the cobra. Several species are found in great numbers in India.

Particularly dangerous is the *cobra-de-capello,* or "hooded snake," so named by the Portuguese because of its ability to spread its neck into a kind of hood. Notorious for the usually fatal outcome of its attacks on humans as well as animals, this snake is likewise revered by the natives of India, some of whom number it among their sacred objects. Thus it is allowed to roam through houses unmolested in its search for mice. It is said that a cobra in the house is considered by the Indian to be an omen of prosperity.

Unlike the rattlesnake, with whose attack most Americans are more familiar, the cobra does not prick two wounds by inserting and immediately withdrawing its fangs. Instead it seems to attempt to chew the victim and makes an ugly wound. Cobra poison affects the nervous system, and unless a powerful anti-venom is administered, the victim of the bite may be dead in a few hours. Probably part of the reverence paid this reptile by the natives results from the fact that their magic "snake stones" do not work on cobra wounds.

Ready to attack, the cobra lifts the front third of its body and uses its long ribs to spread its neck skin. Usually, it is said, the natives suffer attacks only to their bare feet and legs, since their clothing on the rest of the body is sufficient protection against the short fangs. In spite of this protection, however, many hundreds of victims of cobra poison die each year in India.

Paul's Photos, Chicago
SMALL SPECIES OF CROCODILE
The natives pictured here are trying to make pets of these crocodiles. If the "croc"
forgets, and snaps at a leg, the trident is driven into his nose.

The reptile feeds on frogs, birds' eggs, and mice. Reaching six and one-half feet in length, it is large for a poisonous snake, but certainly not the largest. According to tradition, it was the Egyptian species of this snake with which Cleopatra took her life nearly twenty centuries ago.

Deadly enemy of the cobra is the mongoose, a weasel-like animal described elsewhere. The mongoose severs the snake's spinal cord by sinking its teeth deep in the neck. Occasionally the mongoose is fatally bitten, but usually its agility and wiry, erect hair protect it from the bite of the ugly, deadly reptile.

PYTHONS

Other species of the many snakes to be found in India are constrictors. Of these the python is one of the most common. The Indian python, like the species found in Africa, crushes its victim to death by slowly coiling about it and gradually squeezing all life out. Usually it attacks birds and small animals which later are devoured. It is interesting that whether in the natural state or in captivity, pythons insist upon killing their own meat. These snakes will actually starve—an especially long, slow process for them—before they will consent to eat dead meat.

Usually found in trees, the python is likewise a skilled swimmer. Its length may exceed thirty feet, although commonly it is considerably shorter. Colored a light brown and spotted attractively with blue and black, the python is considered one of the most beautiful of reptiles. In its natural habitat, where it is always more healthy than in captivity, the coat reflects a shiny and iridescent glow, greatly enhancing the natural colors.

For their color, their size, and their interesting habits, pythons have been put on exhibit in many zoos and even more side shows. They do not thrive in captivity, never become "tame" in the real sense, and often choose to starve rather than continue such an existence. Forced feeding is usually resorted to in this case, and the body of a chicken or small animal is pushed down the unwilling python's throat.

SEA SNAKES

One of the most interesting of all reptiles is the little sea serpent, less than three feet long, found in the Indian Ocean. Extremely poisonous, eel-like, and an excellent swimmer, this snake has no fishlike gills, but comes regularly to the surface for air. Black stripes on a yellow background make a most attractively colored tail on this curious little creature. Its belly is also bright yellow, sharply differentiated in line from the all-black upper body. Out of water the sea serpent finds movement very difficult. It is truly a natural curiosity and rarely seen.

While the python represents the constrictor type of snake, and the cobra the poisonous snakes of India, in the Ganges and Brahmaputra Rivers are found immense thirty-foot relics of the Reptilian Age. These are two species of crocodiles known as gavials. In the heavy, slimy waters of these rivers, as they flow through the forested regions of the country, can be seen the pointed nose

Courtesy Chicago Park District

THE BLUE PEACOCK OF INDIA AND ASIA

and the greenish, catlike eyes, as the gavial hides from man. Generally timid, and avoiding man or the larger animals, this ungainly, leathery-looking reptile will usually take to the water upon the appearance of danger. On land the length of body and tail makes its movements unwieldy. Its short legs make it difficult to raise body and tail off the ground.

Carnivorous, the crocodile feeds mainly on fish, although it will eat any flesh available. Thus it was a part of one of the cruelest religious rites ever practiced. Formerly, in order to appease the gods during sickness or other unfortunate periods, parents in India were wont to cast their children into the Ganges to the crocodiles as sacrifices. In one month in 1801 twenty-three such cases occurred. The practice has since been discontinued.

It is because of the belief that this reptile always cries after devouring its victim that we have the term "crocodile tears" in our vocabulary.

Courtesy Chicago Park District

THE GREEN PEACOCK OF INDIA AND ASIA

PHEASANTS, PEACOCKS, AND OTHER BIRDS

An American is apt to think of the ringneck pheasant as a bird native to his country, but it is an imported bird, and India was its original and natural home. As is so common in many animals, the name is derived from a characteristic of the male which has a bronze-colored body, yellow sides, and black markings shaped like bars on its long tail. The head is black and around its neck is a white collar, giving the bird its name. The females, which are usually in a flock separate from that of the cocks, are of dull brown coloring. Preferring moist thickets, these birds roost on the ground and eat insects and seeds.

Along the northern border of India, on the slopes of the Himalayas, is found the silver pheasant. This is the largest and best-known of the Asiatic species and is long crested and dark. Also on the slope of these mountains lives the Impeyan pheasant with iridescent, dark plumage.

The peacock, a kind of pheasant, is also native to India and Ceylon. Mature peacocks range in length from thirty-eight to forty-five inches. The head, neck, and breast are rich purple with gold and green reflections. The back is green, and the wings, inner coverts, and shoulders are white, streaked with black. The middle coverts are deep blue, while the abdomen is black. The peacock has a crest of twenty-four feathers webbed only at the tip. In the display before his mates, the male has a proud strut and unfolds his brilliant plumage with striking effects. The female, the pea-hen has more somber colors and no train.

Among the other birds of India are eagles, falcons, hawks, parrots, kingfishers, herons, and pigeons.

Courtesy Field Museum of Natural History, Chicago

AFRICAN ELEPHANTS IN PLAYFUL MOOD

This exhibit is considered one of the finest ever done by the internationally famous American naturalist Carl Akeley. These skins were prepared for mounting by Dr. Edmund C. Heller.

AUSTRALIA

THE GREATER PART of Australia's population lives in the eastern and southeastern parts of the continent. But beyond the pales of these small civilized areas there extends a vast territory of jungles, deserts, forests, and mountains—the bush—that harbors some of the strangest animals the world has ever seen. Having been isolated from the rest of the world for millions of years, Australia has managed to preserve forms of animal and vegetable life that lived ages ago and that have since disappeared from everywhere else but this country which has truly been called the "land of living fossils."

Deep in the hidden fastnesses of Australia's towering eucalyptus forests, surrounded by forests of trees of shorter stature, harbored by lofty karri pines, tree ferns, grass trees, and sweet-smelling acacias, are many strange birds: brilliantly colored cockatoos, lyre birds with their gorgeous tails, kookaburra birds that laugh like jackasses, and kea birds that kill sheep. In the forests and the open plains are the various species of kangaroos, the national animal of Australia, hopping comically on their long hind legs. Moving sluggishly beside streams are strange mammals which have the bill of a duck and lay eggs like a bird. Nuzzling for ants are echidna ant-eaters under curiously shaped bottle-trees, in vegetation that exists now in other parts of the world only in fossil form.

With its collection of strange animals, curious birds, towering forests, vast plains, and aboriginal tribes of "bushmen," Australia presents as interesting a theater of natural wonders as can be found on any section of the earth.

Courtesy Mason Warner, Chicago

KANGAROO MOTHER AND YOUNG
The youngster quite often dives head first into the pouch, then turns around and
peeks out to see what scared him.

AUSTRALIAN MARSUPIALS

Of primary importance, perhaps, among the animals of Australia, are its marsupials, or pouched animals. With the exception of the American family of opossums, marsupials can be found in their natural habitat only in Australia. The marsupials differ from the mammals of the other continents of the world in several interesting ways. The young are born in a very immature and help-less condition, and must be carried in a special brood pouch on the abdomen of the mother. The young are attached to the nip-ples of the mammary glands and receive nourishment until they are able to live independently. In some marsupials the pouch opens from the top; in others from the bottom, and in a few the pouch is merely a fold in the skin.

The marsupials are of considerable interest to biologists. It is a very striking fact that all of the native animals of Australia are marsupials. It is even more striking that they have become diver-sified into various types which superficially resemble animals of other continents. Thus there are marsupial "bears," "wolves," "badgers," "hyenas," "cats," "rabbits," "jumping mice," "wood-chucks," "moles" and "mice." All of these carry the young in the brood pouch in much the same way that the kangaroo and opossum do.

THE GREAT GRAY KANGAROO

Most important and largest of the marsupials is the great gray kangaroo. Full-grown, the male has been known to stand eight feet high. Ordinarily, its body is about four feet long while its tail, a heavy, elongated appendage, tapers to about four feet. Its hind legs are extraordinarily long and powerfully built and have only four instead of five toes. Its third toe is the principal part of the foot; it is almost twelve inches long with a ponderous claw at the end. It is this toe that aids in making possible the amazing hops that constitute the kangaroo's means of locomotion. The first two toes have smaller claws and are used for scratching and cleaning purposes. The fourth toe also helps the kangaroo to make its long hops.

A PAIR OF CONTENTED "JOEYS" OR BABY KANGAROOS

On its head, which is about the size of a collie dog's, are two large ears which are acutely sensitive to sounds. This acuteness is due in part to the fact that they can be rotated to the front or to the rear. It has rather medium-sized brown eyes, and a long snout. Its cleft lips and two large incisor teeth in the front of its lower jaw are very useful in snipping grass and leaves. Its fur is soft and sometimes woolly, but its hide is so duarble when tanned that it is used in place of kid leather in fine shoes. Because it is tight-grained, its strength is almost 17% greater than that of any other leather. It is as soft as kid leather, will not scuff, and although it looks like kid, it can be distinguished from it by tiny surface pocks, caused by fly-bites.

When grazing or ambling slowly along, the kangaroo walks on all four feet, the upper part of its body decidedly lower than the rear because of its relatively short forepaws. But when it is disturbed and takes flight, it straightens up, using its tail as a

Courtesy Mason Warner, Chicago

THIS BOUNDING KANGAROO WAS PHOTOGRAPHED FROM A MOTOR CAR
TRAVELING AT FORTY MILES AN HOUR

prop. Then, with the use of its long toes, powerful hind legs, and amazing tail, it propels itself in a series of fifteen-foot hops that carry it forward at a tremendous speed, while its tail is used to maintain equilibrium, somewhat like a tight-rope walker uses a pole to balance himself. Horses and dogs are usually used for hunting the kangaroo, but of late the Australians have resorted to automobiles. When a great number have to be caught because they have been denuding the sheep pastures of grass, they are rounded together into a pen and slaughtered. The flesh is eaten by Australian aborigines, and a soup made of its tail is eaten by white men when no other food is available.

In the larger kangaroos the period of gestation is about three weeks. When the baby kangaroo is born it is only about an inch long, blind, devoid of hair, but with its hind paws well developed and clawed. Its manner of reaching the mother's pouch is debated by experts. Some say that the mother lifts it to the pouch where it fastens onto one of the mammary glands, suckles, and remains until it is able to take care of itself. Other experts claim, probably with more accuracy, that, with its developed hind legs and claws, it is able to ascend to the pouch unaided. Before it is strong enough to make its own way, but after it is able to eat other food besides milk, the baby kangaroo sticks its head out of the pouch while its mother is grazing, and takes a few nips of grass and leaves for itself. The baby begins to venture out after four months, but hurries back if danger threatens. When it is young, the Australians call the kangaroo a "Joey"; full-grown, he is a "Boomer," "Forester," or "Old Man"; before she has borne young, the female is called a "Flying Doe."

Altogether, there are about sixteen different groups of kangaroos in which there are about one hundred and twenty-nine living species. Of these, the red or woolly kangaroo is second in size to the great gray kangaroo. Where the latter frequents the plains only, the former inhabits the mountain regions also. The only radical differences between the two are in color and size. A still smaller species, the tree kangaroo, differs in that it has not developed as large a jumping claw on its third toe as have the other species. It spends most of its time in the trees, making long leaps from limb to limb with its powerful hind legs.

THE WALLABY

To the Australians the wallaby is not a kangaroo. But, strictly speaking, it is a species of kangaroo varying only in size and color. Of these, the brush kangaroo is the largest; its name is derived from the fact that it lives in the "brush," the dense jungles of Australia. Next in size is the red-necked wallaby, followed by the hare wallaby, which resembles a hare, and the rat kangaroo, or *potoroo*, as it is known by the natives. The last named is about the size of a rabbit but, in spite of its size, it follows almost perfectly the various characteristics of the kangaroo. From this midget rat kangaroo to the bulking great gray kangaroo, the scientist is able to witness a graphic picture of the effects of environment and the manner in which a natural adaptation to it is made.

Courtesy Mason Warner, Chicago

A GROUP OF YOUNG WALLABIES AT THE JENOLAN CAVES, AUSTRALIA

Courtesy Mason Warner, Chicago

A ROCK WALLABY AT THE JENOLAN CAVES, AUSTRALIA

Although the kangaroo breeds well and thrives in captivity, it has never been successfully immunized against the dread effects of actinomycosis, a fungus disease which infects the kangaroo through a lesion in the mouth. Although they are high-strung and nervous, they are quite manageable in captivity and can be trained to put on boxing shows with their forepaws encased in gloves. Occasionally, a 'roo forgets his manners and boxing gloves and strikes out with his murderous, clawed hind feet.

THE PHALANGERS

Also numerous in Australia are the phalangers, mouselike animals which vary in length from a few to about twenty inches.

THE DORMOUSE
PHALANGER

Courtesy American
Museum of Natural History

Although the many species differ in size, shape, and color, they all have large-sized claws especially adapted for tree-climbing. They also have the second and third toes of their hind feet joined. All have long, prehensile tails with which they swing between boughs and trees. They make their food forays at night and although a few exist mainly on herbs, most of them eat anything from bugs, insects, and small birds to roots and herbs.

Most numerous is the common phalanger. Because its face looks something like a fox, it has received the name vulpine phalanger. It is generally about eighteen inches in length and sports a tail about twelve inches long. Above, its fur is a brownish gray; below, it is a dirty yellow-white; its tufted ears are usually white and its tail is black. The natives find its flesh quite succulent because, in feeding, it prefers the leaves of the peppermint gum and the result is a peppermint-flavored meat. When it goes out at night looking for food, it seizes hold of its prey, crushes the head, and partakes first of the brain. The ring-tailed phalanger has a slimmer, white-tipped tail, bare on the under-tip. Its teeth, too, differ from the usual phalanger. Another variation is in the fact that it is the only one of its kind to fashion a nest for itself in the underbrush or in a tree.

THE FLYING PHALANGERS

Just as there is a popular misconception that sailfish and flying squirrels actually fly, so is there an erroneous belief that the flying phalangers are able to propel themselves through the air like birds. The truth of the matter is that they have developed an extension of skin from the wrist of the forepaw to the ankle of the hind leg. When a flying phalanger leaps from one tree to another, it spreads its paws wide and stretches this flap of skin so that the animal seems to be flying. There is no doubt that the extra web of skin enables it to glide, and, at times, the creature's tail functions as a rudder. But it cannot sustain itself in flight and the area of its glide is limited by the original impetus of its leap.

The largest of the flying phalangers is the great flying phalanger which attains a length of twenty inches with a tail almost as long as the body. The web of skin in this species is not as notice-

THE AUSTRALIAN
FLYING
PHALANGER

Courtesy Field Museum
of Natural History

THE AUSTRALIAN
OPOSSUM

Courtesy   Mason   Warner,
Chicago

able as it is in the smaller animals. The fur is soft and silky, of intermixed black and brown, with white on the belly. The smaller species is called the sugar squirrel or squirrel opossum and is a trifle shorter than its cousin, the great flying phalanger. Its fur, too, is as soft as a fluff-ball, but it is dark gray above and white below with a dark stripe running down the back from the tip of the nose to the tip of the tail. At night, when these animals are at their best, they can be seen darting about from tree to tree, seemingly flying with the ease of the man on the trapeze. The smallest species, the pigmy flying phalanger, is only about five inches long, but its agility and extraordinary mobility in the air have earned for it the scientific name of *Acrobates pygmaea*. As small as it is, it is a true marsupial in that it possesses the usual pouch for suckling and protecting its young.

THE KOALA "BEAR"

Children, particularly, delight in watching the antics of this fluff of fur, not only because of its agility in climbing trees but

Courtesy Mason Warner, Chicago

FIVE LITTLE KOALA BEARS WONDERING WHAT TO DO NEXT

Courtesy Mason Warner, Chicago

CLOSE-UP OF THE ALWAYS-INTERESTING KOALA BEAR OF AUSTRALIA

because it is a perfect living model of the "Teddy bear." When full-grown it is about twenty-four inches in length, has a small head, small ears, and an ashen gray coat of fluffy fur which, because it is cheap and durable, is being used in large quantities for wearing apparel. It lives on buds and shoots of the gum tree and eucalyptus tree and seldom travels from its tree habitat. When the young koala has outlived the need of its mother's pouch, it transfers the scene of its activities to her back, to which it clings tenaciously as the mother climbs trees and branches in search of food. Because of its mild disposition and cunning appearance, it is often tamed and kept as a household pet.

THE WOMBAT

The wombat, also known as the Australian badger, is not as formidable an animal as its name might suggest. Its length seldom exceeds thirty-six inches but, because of its tendency to grow fat, its weight, one hundred and fifty pounds at times, makes it appear top-heavy and causes it to waddle ludicrously when it walks. The flesh is edible and, because of the amount of the catch, the wombat is often hunted. The pelt with its thick hide and long, rough hair is not considered useful for wearing apparel. Being sharp-clawed, its feet serve excellently in burrowing holes for its home. Its coloring varies from a brownish yellow to a gray or grayish black.

THE BANDICOOT

In some respects, the bandicoot looks like a large wharf-rat; it has the same body, tail, and sharp nose as its counterpart. It differs in that its ears are oversize, almost like a rabbit's, and its hind legs are miniatures of the kangaroo's. The fur is long and silky, gray along the back, yellowish red on the sides, and white along the belly. Ordinarily, the bandicoot eats only worms, insects, roots, and berries. But it can and does eat almost anything, especially the crops of cultivated fields. For this reason farmers consider it a pest. When the bandicoots become too destructive, they are hunted out of their burrows and occasional nests and killed. The flesh, when baked, makes a tasty food, although some find the skinned carcass repulsive because of its similarity to a rat.

Courtesy Mason Warner, Chicago

MOTHER WOMBAT WITH DAY-OLD BABY

Courtesy Field Museum of Natural History

THE RABBIT-BANDICOOT OF AUSTRALIA

THE TASMANIAN DEVIL

Aptly named is the Tasmanian devil, a flesh-eating marsupial with sharp-pointed and knife-edged teeth suitable for rending flesh. Resembling a badger in appearance, the Tasmanian devil is large-headed like a boar, short-snouted, about twenty inches long with a tail about six inches in length, and with fur that is almost always an intense black, occasionally sprinkled with white hairs. A shield of white covers its chest from the throat to the belly and sometimes continues up to the flanks and shoulders. The Tasmanian devil, in temperament, is everything that the name implies. Ugly, unfriendly, and ferocious, it issues from its burrow or rock cleft at night and seizes upon animals that are often larger than itself, ripping and slashing the flesh with its sharp teeth. Nothing, it seems, can escape its ferocity and it will attack if only for the sake of killing and tearing the flesh. Even in captivity, it retains its sullen defiance and no amount of kindness or feeding can cajole it into a semblance of docility. Because of its destructive habits, it has been decimated in the populous regions so that, at present, it ranges only in the wilds.

Like the Tasmanian devil, the Tasmanian wolf, also called a "tiger," is a ferocious animal that has been eradicated from cultivated areas because of the damage it inflicts upon flocks. Built like a large dog, it averages about four feet in length, including a tail half as long as the body. Its forepart is of a yellowish-brown color, while the rear, from the shoulders to the root of the tail, is striped around the body like a zebra, with black stripes on yellow. It is for this reason that some call it the "zebra wolf" although others refer to it simply as "the tiger." It, too, is a marsupial, carrying its young in a pouch which, varying from the norm, opens backward. It will attack anything, even the spiny anteater which most carnivores avoid because of its arrow-like spines. It must be hunted with dog packs because, singly, a dog has no chance with this ferocious beast. However, unlike the Tasmanian devil, the Tasmanian wolf loses its fierceness when caged and can become friendly, though not domesticated.

Courtesy American Museum of Natural History

THE TASMANIAN DEVIL

Courtesy American Museum of Natural History

THE TASMANIAN WOLF WITH TWO YOUNG PUPPIES

THE DINGO DOG

The only large wild animal in Australia that is not a marsupial is the dingo, a wild dog that roams the bush and wooded areas. The dingo, however, is not a true native of Australia. Because of its large, sharp-pointed ears and bright eyes, it bears some resemblance to the Alaskan malamute dog, but in no other way are the animals similar. Its fur is usually red or brownish yellow in color, although sometimes it varies to black flecked with yellow. Ordinarily, its belly is lighter in shade and around its throat is a scruff of long, shaggy hair. Its tail is long and bushy and the tip is white, as are its paws.

Dingoes are born killers, making raids on sheep flocks and poultry farms and killing much more than they can eat. Since these dogs are swift of foot and have a keen sense of smell, the natives capture them when they are puppies and train them to hunt. Once returned to the dingo flock, however, they revert to their wild habits. Unlike the ordinary dog, the dingo does not bark, but at night it can be heard howling dismally. How the dingo got to Australia is a mystery; evidently it was carried over with the earliest human inhabitants or by some wandering boat from the Asian mainland hundreds of years ago.

THE MONOTREMES—LIVING FOSSILS OF THE ANIMAL KINGDOM

The egg-laying mammals or monotremes furnish other examples of the bizarre nature of the Australian animals. The only two living representatives of this group, the "duckbill" (platypus) and the spiny anteater (echidna) are native to the continent. They have little in common as far as appearance is concerned, but are nevertheless closely related. These queer forms are the most primitive of all the fur-bearing animals. They differ from all other mammals in several important ways. In the first place, they lay eggs with much yolk, like those of the reptiles and birds. Although all mammals develop from eggs, in all except the monotremes the eggs have no yolk and develop within the

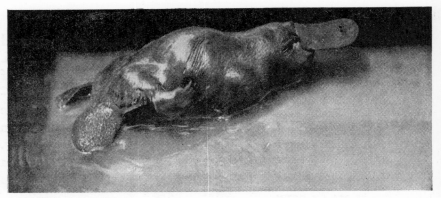

Courtesy Mason Warner, Chicago

PICTURE OF "SPLASH," THE FAMOUS PLATYPUS

body of the mother. The egg-laying habit of these primitive mammals, along with other characteristics, shows rather clearly that they descended from reptiles in ages past.

When the young hatch from the eggs they feed on milk from the mother. But even in this respect these animals are primitive, for the mother does not have teats—the milk is secreted onto the abdomen from small pores.

Called a living fossil because it is undoubtedly a relic of some long-forgotten age, the duckbill is one of the strangest animals in the entire animal kingdom. It has, for instance, among other odd characteristics, a bill like a duck's, a tail like a beaver's, the soft, brown fur of a seal, and clawed, webbed feet with which it either swims in the water or burrows into the ground.

Its oval-shaped body is about twenty inches long from the tip of the bill to the end of the tail, and covered with a loose-fitting coat of seal-like fur. The clawlike toes on the paws are webbed, and the webbing extends past the claws. When swimming the platypus uses the entire web, but when it is burrowing it draws the web back on the palm. The hind foot also has a web, but it is smaller than that on the forepaw. On the inner side of the hind leg of a male platypus is a spur, like a game-cock's, that is hollow like a snake's fang and through which is ejected a poisonous fluid which results in painful swellings.

The young are naked when hatched, and the mother clasps them to her abdomen by her large, beaver-like tail, which curls around them. The young have teeth but soon lose them, and the adults feed by grubbing about in the mud for worms, insects, and other small animals, which they crush within their horny bills. They live in burrows along streams. These burrows may be thirty feet long, with one entrance below water and another above. This arrangement affords protection, as they can enter the nest without being seen. Although the duckbill's smelling and hearing faculties are keen, its eyesight is limited because its eyes are so placed as to make horizontal vision practically impossible. The base of its bill extends into a hard shield that protects the eyes. The ears have a sort of earlid, a fold in the skin, which can be opened and closed at will.

Because it is shy, high-strung, and delicately constituted, the platypus has seldom been put on exhibition in a zoo. The New York Zoölogical Park spent nine years and $1,400 trying to obtain

THE AUSTRALIAN ECHIDNA

one for the Bronx Zoo. It did succeed in getting one, the only live platypus to leave Australia, but it lived for only forty-nine days. The body was stuffed and put into the Newark Museum. The "wild zoo" near Healesville, Australia, boasts of one that is occasionally on exhibition. Caught when it was only five months old, "Splash," the captive platypus, has grown from a fifteen-inch animal weighing forty-two ounces to twenty-three inches, weighing four pounds. Nightly, it eats a fourth of its weight in worms and steamed eggs. When it is not swimming or burrowing, it either preens its fur with its duck-bill like a bird, or combs its hair with its claws.

The spiny anteater, or echidna, is much like a porcupine, with its eighteen inches of body covered with hair and short, sharp quills. Instead of teeth, it has a tube-like snout out of which protrudes a long tongue covered with a sticky fluid. When hunting for ants, the echidna sticks its nose into an anthill, pushes its tongue through the aperture and reaches around for ants, which stick to the tongue. Then it draws the tongue back into its mouth together with the adhering ants. Its sharp claws serve both for ripping open ant nests and for burrowing. In escaping an enemy, it can dig itself into a burrow in a very short time. But if it hasn't time to burrow, it simply rolls itself up into a ball, projects its spines, and dares its attackers to do something about it.

The echidna, only living relative of the platypus, lays two eggs at a time. The eggs, about the size of a sparrow's, are deposited in a pouch on the abdomen. Here they hatch, and the young remain in the pouch for a few weeks.

THE KOOKABURRA AND THE LYRE BIRD

The penguin has often been called the comedian of the bird world. If such is the case, then it should have for its audience a flock of kookaburras, or Australian laughing jackass birds. The moment the sun comes up the kookaburra begins laughing—loud, raucous laughter that is amazingly human. About the size of a crow, with a flat head and a longish beak, the kookaburras are

Courtesy Mason Warner, Chicago

AUSTRALIAN MAGPIE AND KOOKABURRA HAVING A FRIENDLY CHAT

quite numerous in Australia. They come from the bush to the cities where they congregate in the parks, streets, and gardens and give voice to their noisy laughter. Because they kill and eat only snakes, mice, frogs, and insects, they are valued by the Australians.

What deep-seated, unknown instinct is it in the male lyre bird that causes it to build a mound for itself on which it stands with its gorgeous, lyre-shaped tail proudly displayed in all its colored splendor? That is just what this remarkable Australian bird does when, during the mating season, its tail is in full growth. The body of the bird is ordinary, of a dull brown color, the quill feathers a somewhat brownish red, but the tail feathers of the male offer a brilliant contrast. The two outer feathers, which are longer than the bird itself, form the frame of a lyre, with the finer tail feathers between forming the strings.

When it is not seeking food or posing on a hillock, the male lyre bird carries its tail horizontal with its body. Like most birds,

Courtesy Australian National Travel Association

THE AUSTRALIAN LYRE BIRD

This beautiful bird from "Down Under" is quite a mimic, capable of imitating anything
from the bark of a dog to the scream of a locomotive whistle.

it moults its feathers in the fall. But, in June, when the mating season begins, it regains its colorful plumage and builds itself a mound to display its splendor to the female. She, on the other hand, is a drab creature with no plumage other than the usual feathers. She lays her one egg in a covered, oval nest, hatches it, and seems satisfied to let her male strut proudly about.

Not only for its fancy dress, but for its artistic accomplishments is the lyre bird an extraordinary creature. The mound which it scrapes together of leaves and twigs serves as a pedestal from which to display its adornment, but in addition is a stage upon which the proud male sings, mimics, and dances with its brilliant tail feathers bent forward, partially concealing itself. But the female in her plain dress never participates in her mate's operatic or terpsichorean performances.

THE AUSTRALIAN BRUSH TURKEY

The Australian brush turkey is about the size of the American turkey, with yellow wattles, dark feathers, and a pinkish, naked head. Interesting about it is the fact that it erects pyramid-shaped mounds, four to six feet in height, and about forty feet in circumference in which to lay its eggs. Mounds of this size are not built in one season nor by a single pair, material being added each year by the turkeys using it. These mounds consist of soil and decaying vegetable matter which the birds scrape into a pile with their feet. As the vegetable matter decomposes, it generates heat which aids in incubating the twelve to sixteen eggs which each turkey hen deposits. The turkeys are socialistically inclined and use a single mound as a communal nesting place. The hen first scratches a hole into the mound about eight or ten inches deep. She deposits her eggs perpendicularly into the hole and departs. The male then struts up to the hole and fills it with vegetable matter and soil which he tramples down firmly. After that, the parents make occasional visits to the mound to see that the encrustation is not so hard that it might prevent the fledglings from breaking through when they are hatched. When the chicks finally are hatched, they appear partly feathered and with fairly well-developed beaks and claws so that they can scratch for themselves immediately.

Courtesy Chicago Park District

THE AUSTRALIAN EMU

THE EMU AND THE CASSOWARY

The emu, a bird that grows as tall as a man, is in many respects like an ostrich. It is of a light brown-and-gray color and its feathers are thick, stringy, and hairy in appearance. It is found in the plains and open forests of Australia but, for some reason, has become quite scarce. Although it cannot fly, it is said to be the fastest running creature on the earth. But when cornered, instead of striking out forward with its long, ponderous, three-toed feet, it kicks sideward and backward like a cow. Odd is the fact that, after the female has laid her eggs, she relinquishes her place to the male, which squats on the eggs for a period of about eight weeks until they are hatched. Even after the striped chicks have broken their shells and have hopped into the world, the male continues to care for them until they are able to take care of themselves. In the female's long neck is a peculiar pouch, an out-pocketing of its windpipe, through which it is able to emit a loud, booming note comparable to the sound of a gong or a muffled drum. The male can only hiss or grunt when angry or disturbed.

Although the cassowary is related to the emu, in coloring it differs greatly from its drab cousin. Its neck, which is somewhat smaller than the emu's, is bare of feathers but has brilliant noduled wattles. On top of its head is a sort of large, horny helmet, also brightly colored. Its plumage is composed of shiny-black quill feathers which look almost like hair.

The cassowary is a dangerous bird when wounded or angered for it can strike forward or backward with its powerful three-toed feet, the middle toe of which is almost club-like and pointed with a barbarous nail, as effective as the kangaroo's claw. These birds have become quite rare, because their skins have been found to make excellent rugs and doormats.

Paul's Photos, Chicago
THE AUSTRALIAN CASSOWARY
Full grown, this bird reaches a height of five feet.

Courtesy Mason Warner, Chicago

THE NEW ZEALAND KIWI

THE KIWI

New Zealand, too, possesses one of the running, wingless birds found in this part of the world—the *apteryx*, called by the natives the kiwi because of its call-note which it issues only in the early night, being silent after midnight when it feeds. It resembles a chick in appearance, but is about the size of a hen. Its feathers look like long, hair-like spines. Its legs are stoutly built with three toes on them, the center one being elongated like the cassowary's. Its bill is long and thin, almost like a tube with spines bristling out of its base. When it hunts for food, it runs with its nose furrowing the ground on the outlook for worms in holes or under roots and, as it searches, it emits a queer, sniffing noise. When angered it growls like a puppy, ruffles its feathers, snaps with its beak and kicks out with its heavily-nailed feet. It is found only in New Zealand where the natives roast it and formerly used its feathers to adorn their ancient ceremonial cloaks.

Courtesy Mason Warner, Chicago

KEAS, OR SHEEP-KILLING PARROTS OF NEW ZEALAND

PARROTS OF NEW ZEALAND

A strange bird, indeed, is the kea, a member of the parrot family found only in New Zealand. It is somewhat the same size as a raven, but its plumage is olive green with many of the feathers edged with black. Its upper bill is hooked over its lower bill and is very sharp. When sheep were first brought over to the island, these birds, which ordinarily ate only berries and fruits, began to feed on the sheep's flesh. They would attach themselves to the animal's back and tear through the skin and flesh until they reached the kidneys. Then they would greedily devour the surrounding fat. They played such havoc with the sheep herds that the government was forced to put a bounty on them.

Another New Zealand parrot is the kakapo, or owl parrot, so called because of the ruffs of feathers around its eyes, which give it an owlish appearance. It is of good size and its plumage is a sort of metallic green specked with yellow and black. Although it

Courtesy Mason Warner, Chicago
WHITE-PLUMED BIRD OF PARADISE OF AUSTRALIA

has wings it cannot fly, and it uses them merely to balance when it climbs trees. Seeming to be well suited for life in the trees, it nevertheless prefers to remain on the ground in holes where it lays its eggs. Like the owl, it is a night bird and forages for its food—roots, herbs, shrubs, and berries—only at that time. Occasionally, it will eat a lizard. When it feeds it is lively and voices its satisfaction with its food with an odd grunting noise. However, because it is not able to fly off the ground, it is steadily being decimated by animals which stalk it in the day when it is loggy and sleepy.

LIZARDS

Not only are there strange mammals and birds in Australia, but there are also lizards which can be found in no other country and which have characteristics to be found in no other species of lizard. The frilled lizard of Queensland and northwestern Australia possesses around its neck a peculiar many-colored collar which is folded up when the lizard is calm but expands like an umbrella when it is disturbed. The frilled lizard averages about two feet in length, is about eight inches in diameter and has a heavy, tapering tail longer than its body which is light brown with transverse bars across it. When traveling long distances on level ground, this strange creature lifts its forelegs into the air and runs like a human being. The Australian water lizard, an excellent swimmer, is also capable of running upright like a man.

The bearded lizard is another of Australia's strange creatures. Projecting from its chin is a beard-like throat membrane that flares into a fan when the lizard becomes excited. It grows to about fifteen inches in length; its scales are very sharp and rough and are capable of cutting the hands of one who handles it carelessly. It sleeps on tree shoots and branches with its legs wrapped around the trunk, like a human being in the attitude of climbing.

Although the mountain devil lizard is small, about six or seven inches in length, its body is so covered with sharp prickles and spines that it is safe from trouble. Since the mountain devil feeds on ants, it is used by the Australians to rid their homes of ant invaders. Some of these lizards have been known to eat as many as fifteen hundred ants at a time.

The lace lizard, also known as the *goanna,* at times attains a length of five or six feet. It particularly likes eggs of all sorts and, when it cannot find eggs of wild birds, it raids chicken coops and eats not only the eggs, but the chickens as well. When these depredations become too common, the farmers organize goanna hunts. In these, the goanna exhibits remarkable feats of agility. But when it is cornered, it sometimes faces about and crawls up the person of one of the hunters, using its long, powerful tail as a whip and inflicting considerable damage with it. The male of this species is usually very colorful in appearance, with a skin that is delicately marked with lacey figurings, from which it received its name. Its throat is ablaze with tintings of blue and yellow.

Courtesy Mason Warner, Chicago

MALAYAN FISHERMAN SPEARING FISH

SOUTH PACIFIC ISLANDS

EAST OF AUSTRALIA, north of the island continent, and northwest of it are the regions known as the South Seas. Since the earliest explorers—Magellan, Drake, Cook, and Captain Bligh—visited these waters, the verdant islands which lie in them have fascinated the minds of men. Far to the east are the Galapagos group with their famous monster turtles; proceeding westward the seamen voyaged to Hawaii, to the craggy Marquesas, to Tahiti, Fiji, Bali, and Java. The largest of the South Sea islands —Sumatra, Java, Borneo, Celebes, and Papua—lie between Australia and the long Malayan finger of Asia. According to geologists the whole area was above water at one time in the world's history, from the southernmost tip of Australia to the northernmost icy point of Siberia, a giant land mass over which animals roamed, early in their development. Some heaving of the earth's mighty shoulders, some enormous shifting of the crust, cut off the Australian world from the world of Asia, leaving some islands connected with one land and some with the other. The separations of these islands came at a still later date. There is an imaginary line passing among these islands, which marks the first great breaking. Separated by the narrow channel of this line, often only a few miles of water, are islands with radically differing plants and animals. The line, called Wallace's Line after A. R. Wallace, the naturalist who defined it, splits romantic Bali and Borneo, with a wild profusion of Asiatic animal life, from Lombok and Celebes in which live no tigers, no elephants, no orangutans, but only the kangaroo, the wallaby, the echidna, and the cassowary—typical Australian animals. The sharp demarcation of this dividing line is a fascinating phenomenon; it is as if two city-dwelling families living next door to each other were not only unacquainted but did not belong to the same world—as if one family was a group of haughty cosmopolitan socialites and the other a family of aborigines. In the narrow channel the land broke, at a time in the life of the earth when there were neither tigers nor kangaroos, but only unknown ancestral types which have long since passed from the face of the earth. The primitive stock developed differently in each of the two great divisions, and it was only yesterday, as geologists figure time, that the smaller islands were separated from the two major land masses.

From the cleavage between Borneo and the Celebes, Wallace's line veers off to the east, leaving the Philippines with the Asiatic group. North of these islands is Formosa, the absorbing island which guards the coast of China. A varied array of animals inhabits China, an assortment which begins with the tropical fauna of the Siamese southern border and includes the animals of temperate climates and the wild life of the cool regions of the north. At the Siberian frontier there is no boundary for animals and the progression is still determined by environment rather than by mere political boundaries. The animals of island Japan, although they exhibit some of the differences characteristic of island isolation, are an interesting group.

LIFE CROWDED AND COMPRESSED

West of Wallace's line are three great islands, Java, Sumatra, and Borneo; the animals which live on them are to a considerable extent those of tropical Asia. The wildest and least civilized of these islands is Borneo, where tropical heat and torrential rainfall produce a luxuriant growth of life which is equaled in few parts of the world. On this great island life is compressed. Hemmed in by the sea there is a rich cross section of plants and animals which furnishes a vast laboratory for the biologist, the student of living things. There are no polar bears and no penguins, but there is scarcely a class of life which is not represented in the congress of animals and plants of Borneo.

Paul's Photos, Chicago

JAVANESE LIZARD

Along the sultry coastline of Borneo, frogs, the most spectacular of which is a flying type, as well as toads and salamanders, live and are prey to that great and spectacular group, the reptiles. Some of the individuals of the reptilian tribe always live near or in the water; others have left it entirely and live on the land. The reptiles range widely in size. Some of the lizards are the size of a man's finger; others grow to much greater dimensions. Some of them can glide through the air. The members of this aerial group are called the flying dragons, although they are not dragons and they cannot really fly. They are small lizards, seldom as long as eight inches, but their appearance actually resembles that of dragons. They are brightly colored little animals flitting about among the leaves of the tropical treetops like rays of the sun. Their wings are merely folds of their gleaming, iridescent skin between their forearms and their bodies, but with these parachute-like appendages they are able to soar from branch to branch. The wings are held rigid by means of half a dozen rib-like bones, and the little lizard truly seems to fly as it soars through space after the insects which it eats.

The turtles are an ingeniously adapted group which has carried the armor-plating of sea animals like oysters to an even more effective extreme. Alligators and their relatives are among the largest and best adapted of all modern reptiles. They are reminiscent of the age of reptiles, when great saurians like the Tyrannasaurus, Brontosaurus, the Ichthyosaurus, and the Pterodactyl-ruled the earth. Probably the most highly specialized of all the reptilian group are the snakes. Here in Borneo they live everywhere—pythons hang their great bodies from the trees, water snakes infest the tropical rivers, and cobras and myriad other varieties slither along the ground throughout the great island. Through the air soar hundreds of kinds of birds, from the mighty eagle, the falcon, and the kite to the lesser flying things such as the swifts, from whose nests the Chinese make their strange bird's nest soup. On the ground are a number of types of beautiful

INDIAN AND ASIATIC PEACOCK

Black Star photo

pheasants, the argus and the fire-back as well as the well-known peacock. The Borneo jungle is a gorgeous moving panorama of animals against a steaming green backdrop of plants. Of all the vertebrates the most spectacular are the mammals, of which group man himself is a member. There are multitudes of small animals such as mice, shrews, squirrels, rats, rabbits, and porcupines. They swarm in the dense, creaking jungle, food for the larger animals, the bears, tiger cats, and the wild boars. The rhinoceros and the elephant, as well as deer, wild oxen, and bats live in this teeming land.

THE MALAYAN SUN BEAR

The Malayan sun bear is one of the most interesting animals of the Borneo jungle. This bear is smaller than the other bears of the world, and his appearance easily distinguishes him from other

Paul's Photos, Chicago

THE PLAYFUL LITTLE HONEY BEAR OF MALAY

types. His short, thick coat is black, and he wears a semicircular shirt front of bright orange, although his cousin on the Malay mainland wears a more conservative white. His nose is also light in color, and his ears are smaller than those of many other types. The sun bear's claws are long and tough, for it is with them that he makes his living in the tropical forest. Much of his diet consists of ants, and with his sharp claws he rips up the great apartment house hills of the tropical ants and termites.

SCALY ANTEATER

There are seven species of anteaters that are to be found in the tropical climates of Asia and Africa. They are also known by the names of Manis and Pangolin. They derive their name of scaly anteaters from the growth that covers their entire bodies with the exception of the underparts. The broad, overlapping, sharp-edged, horny scales are rather large over the central part of the body, and become somewhat smaller on the limbs, neck, and head. There are hairs growing between these scaly growths.

The animals obtain their food with a long wormlike tongue, which is covered with a viscous fluid, to which ants and termites stick when the anteater plunges it into an anthill. Their feeding hours are always during the night.

Against their enemies the scaly anteaters present a most formidable defense by rolling themselves into a ball. In this state they form a mass of scales which is almost impenetrable. They are able to resist even the efforts of a grown man who attempts to unroll them.

Ordinarily, they grow to a length of from one to three feet. Some African species, however, are said to reach a length of six feet, including the tail, which, in all cases, is equal to or twice the length of the body itself.

The African anteater differs from the Asiatic variety in the matter of ears. The latter has small external ears, while the former has none.

THE SWINGING ORANGUTAN

But probably the most interesting of all are the apes and jabbering monkeys: a tarsius monkey, several kinds of macaques, and

Courtesy Chicago Park District

"BARNEY," THE FOUR-HUNDRED-POUND ORANGUTAN IN
LINCOLN PARK ZOO, CHICAGO

"Barney" is said to be the largest and heaviest Sumatran Orangutan in captivity.

many other varieties including the man-like gibbon. The fascination which the orangutan holds for men is almost unequaled; this creature, so much like man in many respects, one of the most highly developed of all the great apes, lives only in the forests of Borneo and Sumatra. The orangutan has nearly all of the characteristics of man, but in a different degree; the only absolute structural difference is that of the heel bone, present in man, but lacking in the great ape. Usually the orangutan travels through the trees of the dense tropical forest, swinging along from bough to bough, along the great looping vines. His arms are very long; like those of the gibbon they hang, when he stands erect, almost to his ankles; they are much longer and stronger than his legs. The hands of the orang are very similar to those of man. There is even a thumb, that most useful of digits, and the long apish fingers are as useful to the orangutan in his life as are those of man. The fingers are slightly webbed, and as the ape swings along through the treetops, he seems almost to be flying.

Traveling on the ground the ape finds much more difficult. He looks like an old man, using his great hanging arms as crutches. The orangutan is a shaggy, red-haired creature, strange in appearance as he crouches on the jungle floor. He is a little old gaffer about four and a half feet high. The shaggy hair on his body is a foot long on the arms and thighs of some individuals. His feet are long and, without a heel bone, their structure resembles his hands more than it does a human foot. The ape's legs are bowed, and to him they must seem a poor means of locomotion indeed, when compared with the swooping, swinging gait made possible by his great arms, which take him along seven feet at a swing. The orang is a strict vegetarian, living on various sorts of roots and shoots. A peaceable citizen of the tropic forest, he seeks the life of none of his neighbors, and few of them are so foolhardy as to attack him, for he is a powerful antagonist when on the defensive. Speculation about the intelligence of this ape is usually futile. Apparently he is not so ingenious as the chimpanzee, but is more so than the gorilla. Certain it is that the ape's mental power is greater than that of any of the other animals, even than that of the monkeys with tails.

THE LITTLE TARSIER WITH BIG EYES

There is another primate, much more primitive than the orangutan, which, with the exception of a single species found in Celebes, dwells in the forests of the islands west of Wallace's line— the tarsier. Apparently the tarsier has remained close to the ancestral stock, and his appearance, which presents many characteristics of the more specialized primates in a primitive form, is indeed odd. The tarsier is a tree-dwelling animal of about the same size as a squirrel, but its tail is not like the bushy plume of the squirrel; it is a long, thin appendage with a tuft at the end like the tassel on the end of a bell rope. The eyes of the tarsier are unbelievably large and they show a rudimentary beginning of the yellow spot found in the eyes of the great apes and man. This yellow spot permits concentration of vision which is directly connected with the growth of intelligence of the apes and man; in the tarsier the spot is diffused. When the sun sinks and night falls on the forest, the tarsier with its great saucer eyes begins to forage for the insects and small lizards which make up its diet. The agile creature is equipped with an unusual bone structure in its legs which enables it to leap easily from bough to bough, and at the tips of its fingers are little sticky spots which enable it to stop suddenly in its graceful boundings high above the jungle floor. The fur of the tarsier is dark brown, and its large ears combine their sensitivity with that of its great eyes to make the little animal completely at home in the dark shifting treetops at night.

Probably the most amazing of the animals found on Borneo and on other tropical islands is the proboscis monkey. This creature is large with a long tail and red hair. His nose, which gives him his name, is tremendously long, almost elephantine in its proportions, extending down beyond his lower jaw.

FLYING LEMUR

The flying lemurs are members of a primitive group of insect-eating mammals, the insectivores. They are related to the tree shrews, found in the same regions, and to the shrews, moles, and hedgehogs of other countries. Unfortunately, the name "insect eater" is not always appropriate because some of the members eat other foods. This little animal goes under other aliases, namely, cobego, and colugo, but they all refer to the same family which frequents many East Indian islands.

Like the flying squirrel, the flying lemur is distinguished from his relatives in that he possesses a membrane on each side of his body, connecting the fore and hind limbs. Also like the flying squirrel, this lemur cannot actually fly, but is able to glide great distances by using the membranous prolongation of his skin. Its rate of descent is about one foot for every five feet of horizontal distance covered.

Sharp, hooked claws distinguish its fingers which undoubtedly aid the flying lemur in clinging to the tree branch on which he

Black Star photo

THE FLYING LEMUR OF INDIA

sleeps during the daytime. The night is spent in quest of food, the favorite items being fruits and leaves.

In size, the flying lemur is comparable to an ordinary-sized cat, with its color ranging from gray to light brown, interspersed with different colored spots and stripes.

TREE SHREWS

In India and Borneo we find the tree shrew, a squirrel-like insectivore with a very pretty appearance. The variety found in Borneo grows to the largest size, with a longer muzzle and an overlapping upper jaw. Its silky hair is of a reddish-brown color tinged slightly with yellow.

Unlike other types of shrews, the tree shrew sallies forth on food-hunting expeditions during the daytime. Scrambling through tree branches, it is extremely delighted to come across insects which it devours with pleasure.

Another type of tree shrew, called the Malayan banxring, is capable of being tamed. Often it is used to keep gardens clear of destructive insects and worms.

All these creatures live—are born, multiply, and die—in the screeching, broiling greenness of the Borneo jungle. All seems to be confusion, but all life is a pattern, a pattern of interdependence, of plant related to plant and animal related to animal and countless even more complex relationships between plant and animal. No one knows where first life began or where the early stages of the development of plants and animals took place. It is certain that if it did begin in one place it quickly spread to many parts of the surface of the earth. In the tropics—and it must be remembered that at times in the history of the earth the tropics included greater and at other times lesser portions of the earth than now—life is more violently exuberant and profuse than in the temperate and arctic regions.

BIRDS OF PARADISE

East of Wallace's line the situation is strangely different. At some point in the world's history an isolation began and the Australian-type animals show entirely separate characteristics. In these islands, consequently, the larger forms of animal life are scarcer. The Celebes, Papua, and the many other islands east of the line have some animals—some of which were imported by man—but they are in the main of distinct types and characteristics. Here lives the beautiful bird of paradise, of which there are dozens of different species throughout the islands of the Pacific. The plumage of the males is a highly specialized sex characteristic which could survive only in lands like these peaceful islands, where predatory animals are very few. The females are much less showy in plumage than the males.

Among these gorgeous creatures are amazingly colored birds whose feathery coats gleam with all the colors of sunlight through a prism. The "great" bird of paradise is not content merely to spread and flash his rosy violet wings, which merge into a rusty yellow and the bright sunny yellow of his back. He sports a brilliant fountain of plumage which streams upward and out-

Courtesy Mason Warner, Chicago

THE WHITE-PLUMED BIRD OF PARADISE
Some idea of the gorgeous coloring of this bird can be gained from the fact that his
breast and throat and the top of his head are a beautiful shade of green while his
collar is white, and legs are yellow.

ward from beneath his wings—a majestic cascade of white and
cream and pink and gold and a hundred other subtle tints. His
throat is a glistening green, a bright emerald set in the beautiful
and ornate brocade of his feathers. Another of these magnificent
creatures is the "kingly" bird of paradise. His back is a rich red
which shades to a rusty brown in wings and tail. The fore
part of his wings is white and a strip of green separates the white
from the reddish-brown. His crowning glory, however, is a pair
of long wiry filaments which extend backward from his tail. Like
black threads these strands stand out, and at their tips they become
spiral green disks, bright green coins at the tip of his tail.

Still another beautiful specimen is the "magnificent" bird of
paradise. This type exhibits a different but equally gorgeous
variety of plumage. His throat and breast are an iridescent blue-
green and his back and wings are green and gold, a flaming gold
that blends into fringe of soft olive green. About his shoulders is

Courtesy Mason Warner, Chicago

THE GOURA PIGEON OF NEW GUINEA
Sometimes referred to as the Crowned Pigeon of Asia.

thrown a gleaming white shawl, tinted with quiet pinks and blues. There are almost half a hundred other kinds of birds of paradise, each with its own particular sort of flamboyant plumage.

THE BABIRUSA AND THE ANOA

Perhaps the most peculiar animal living in Celebes is a strange-looking pig, the babirusa. The tusks of the males, instead of curving upward along the outside of the upper jaw as in other pigs, grow through the top of the snout and curve backward almost touching the forehead. The name of this grotesque beast means "pig-deer," but there is no relationship whatever to the deer. The skin is dark gray and very wrinkled. In the wild state, the babirusa roam in herds through the jungle and along the river banks where they afford excellent sport for the natives.

Another remarkable animal found only in Celebes is the anoa, a small antelope-like buffalo. It is said to be the smallest of the hollow-horned ruminants, a group including the oxen, buffalo, bison, and the musk-ox. The anoa has small straight horns which project backward from the top of the head. The color is generally of a dark brown or black, and the height is slightly over three feet.

North of Celebes lies a group of islands known as the Philippines. They are regarded as the remnants of a former extension of the Asiatic continent which extended all the way from the mainland by way of Formosa to the island of Borneo.

In the dense forests of Mindoro, one of the Philippine Islands, is found a small black buffalo which is closely related to the anoa of Celebes. The tamarau, as it is called by the natives, is about three and one-half feet tall and possesses small upright horns which curve slightly inward. This remarkable little buffalo is thought by many people to be a hybrid between the anoa and the Indian buffalo.

KING COBRA

This is a very large, venomous serpent that is also known as the hamadryad. Although it has a rather wide range, from the Philippine Islands to Ceylon, the fact that it is comparatively rare keeps it from being the most deadly reptile in the world. It exhibits no fear of man, and will attack him without reason. A man will often succumb to its bite within a few minutes, and an elephant in less than two hours. Living chiefly in damp heavily wooded regions, it attains a length of twelve feet and sometimes more.

Curiously enough, the food of the king cobra consists chiefly of other snakes, even the common cobra. The usual method of attack is to grasp the victim just behind the head, and then swallow the unfortunate creature head first.

The coloring of the adult is usually brown, accompanied by dark crossbands.

KING COBRA OF INDIA AND OTHER PARTS OF ASIA

DRAGON LIZARD

Like most other animals, the dragon lizard also is the owner
of more than one name, often being referred to as the giant lizard
and monitor lizard. Although most lizards possess ugly and terrifying features, they are usually of a placid disposition. Such,
however, is not the case with the dragon lizard. This animal is
one who can take care of himself very handily, and usually he can
take care of an enemy with equal ease. The largest lizard in the
world, his twelve feet of fighting power make a foe to reckon
with. Lizards of this size inhabit Komodo in the East Indies, where
the natives live in great fear of them. Their fears are so great
that they imagine a young dragon lizard to be more deadly than
any other reptile.

The dragon lizard's principal food is rather large game, including wild pigs. They venture forth during the day in search
of food, remaining in dens among the rocks at night.

Courtesy Chicago Park District

THE CAMEL IN WINTER DRESS

ANIMALS OF CHINA AND CENTRAL ASIA

BECAUSE China is primarily composed of large tracts of sparsely inhabited areas, and because of wide variations in elevation and climate, there are to be found in its confines numerous species of animals. The habits and characteristics of many of the animals are equivalent to those of varieties found in the southeastern United States. One of the main reasons for this similarity is that both areas lie on the eastern ends of continents and are about equally distant from the equator.

The list of China's animal population includes such common varieties as wolves, foxes, panthers, leopards, tigers, civet cats, martens, brown and black bears, elephants, rhinoceroses, muskrats, hares and rabbits, and a host of others.

There are, however, species that are peculiar to China. For instance, this country is the home of the silkworm. Actually, it is not a worm, but the caterpillar of a Bombycid moth. It inhabits the northern provinces of China, for the most part. The food that enables it to spin perfect silk is the mulberry leaf. It can be fed other leaves but the resulting silk will be of an inferior quality. The time of life in the caterpillar stage is about four weeks. The length of fiber in a cocoon ranges from eight hundred to a thousand yards. The natives not only use the spun material of the cocoon as silk, but also make use of the "worms" themselves in preparation of a food which is considered quite a delicacy.

Northwest of China, beyond the Great Wall, lies the immense Gobi desert, which some scientists have regarded as the cradle of humanity from which all races migrated to other parts of the

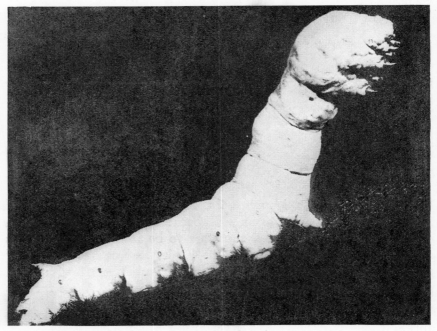

Courtesy International Silk Guild

FULL-GROWN SILK WORM, HEAD RAISED, IT IS READY TO BEGIN
SPINNING THE COCOON

world. History tells us that many tribes from this region literally swarmed over eastern Europe and Asia Minor at various times.

However, the Gobi region has not always been a desert. Evidence has been found in the form of fossil dinosaurs which seems to prove that the area once supported a large animal population. The change in climatic conditions since then has resulted in the present typical desert fauna that is found there.

To the north, the Gobi gives way to the steppes, a typical grassland savanna which harbors two distinct groups of animals. The short grass areas provide ranges for the suslick or squirrel, wolf, rabbit, fox, and a number of rodents. The older areas are covered with long grass and there we find such animals as the jumping rabbit and saiga antelope. Of all the animals inhabiting the steppes the saiga antelope is perhaps the most curious in appearance.

SAIGA ANTELOPE

This moose-nosed animal is closely related to the gazelles. The inflated appearance of its nose is caused by the position and size of the nasal bones. Its countenance is somewhat sheeplike, more noticeably so in the female than in the male. Only the male has horns, which are of a peculiar amber color, and about thirteen or fourteen inches in length. In color, the saiga antelope is dull yellow in summer and nearly white in winter. Its coat resembles that of a sheep in its fleeciness. It exhibits some sheeplike habits—jumping and butting, in particular.

Hunters have great difficulty in trapping this specimen. Its keen senses of hearing, sight, and smell make it extremely elusive, and only the most expert of museum specimen-hunters succeed in capturing it.

The swollen-looking nose of the saiga may appear ludicrous, but it serves a very useful purpose. Since its habitat is the plains regions, it is subjected to periodic dust storms, when its nose acts as a filter, enabling the animal to breathe normally and comfortably without filling its lungs with dust.

During the time of Paleolithic man, saiga antelopes roamed over western Europe. Caves of France, Belgium, and Great Britain have yielded remains of them.

SIBERIAN ARGALI

These argali sheep are the largest members of the sheep family. They are distinguishable by their immense horns, which often measure forty-eight inches along the curve, and are about fourteen inches in circumference at the root.

In Siberia these animals have been killed off by Tatars who hunted them from horseback, but the species still can be found near the timberline in the high areas of Mongolia. Their color is ordinarily dark gray, and their wool is hidden by hair. A Tibetan argali called the nyan closely resembles the Mongolian species. The bighorn sheep of North America have often been referred to as American argali sheep.

MARCO POLO SHEEP

Marco Polo, the original globe-trotter, was the first to describe these sheep found in the high plateaus of the Pamirs, and consequently they bear his name, or Ovis Poli.

Only the Siberian argali, the largest of all sheep, exceeds a Marco Polo ram in size. The latter usually attains a weight of about three hundred pounds.

Preferring hills and grassy plains for both safety and food, the Marco Polo variety rarely descends to lower than twelve thousand feet above sea-level, although in the Thian-shan Mountains there have been reports of its descending to two or three thousand feet.

PANDAS

The panda is a small carnivorous animal, often called the bear-cat. The panda itself resembles a cat, with its thick, long coat of reddish-brown fur. Its ears are high-pointed, with a touch of black coloring below them. Its tail is very bushy and about as long as the body itself. Red and yellow rings feature the coloring of the tail.

The southeastern Himalayas provide the panda's home grounds. It is usually found among trees and rocks, which it can negotiate with great dexterity.

The giant panda is the link by which the panda is connected to the raccoon family. It is bearlike in appearance and action. Its coloring, too, is very different from the ordinary panda.

Its face and the upper part of the neck are white, and the eyes and ears are black. The forelegs, shoulders, hind legs, and hindquarters are covered with black fur, but the middle section of its body is white.

At the present time, there are only two giant pandas in captivity, of which one is located at the Brookfield Zoo near Chicago, Illinois. It was captured in eastern Tibet, as was the second one, which is on its way to the same zoo.

Courtesy American Museum of Natural History

THE GIANT PANDA

(After a painting by A. A. Janssen.)

A Plantigrade animal related to the racoon, discovered in 1869 by the French explorer Abbé David. The panda's range is in western and southern China, also in northeastern India. He is found in the higher elevations, between six and fourteen thousand feet, where his very thick black and white fur keeps him warm and comfortable. In the wild state the panda lives largely on bamboo shoots, but the specimen in the Brookfield Zoo, near Chicago, is thriving on a diet of celery, lettuce, fruits, porridge, and milk.

THE DANGEROUS WILD BOAR

A relative of the common farm swine is the wild boar. Although the latter is much larger, it is also far superior in speed and agility. The defensive features of wild boars include a rather thick skin to minimize the bites of attackers, and a pair of formidable tusks that are very effective in warding off enemies. As the boars advance in age, their tusks come upward, thereby lessening their usefulness as fighting weapons; but, on the other hand, the upper teeth begin to come outward, as though Nature were endeavoring to provide a substitute weapon that the boar might use in fighting. The characteristic nose, ending in a flat disk, is of such toughness that they are able to use it in turning up the soil to search for worms and roots, which they prefer as food.

In keeping with the common conception of pigs, wild boars are extremely fond of wallowing in mud or water. However, they take great care first to "look for the nearest exit" in case their recreational period is rudely interrupted by some larger animal in search of a meal.

The social habits of male and female wild boars are quite different. It is not unusual to see bands of sows and young pigs roaming together in search of food. Boars, especially the older ones, are just the opposite; they are ordinarily found alone, and apparently prefer a solitary existence.

THE ASIATIC CAMEL

The camel is ordinarily thought of as being restricted to the great Sahara Desert. However, Central Asia is the home of the Bactrian camel, distinguished by its two dorsal humps. These humps, incidentally, are not for carrying water, as is usually supposed, but are storing places for fat, allowing the animal to travel great distances without eating. Expeditions that may use thousands of camels in a march carry surprisingly little food for the animals. Camels will usually eat any vegetation that is green, thereby requiring constant vigilance against poisonous shrubs and leaves.

Courtesy Chicago Park District

ASIATIC CAMELS

The animals carry their much publicized water supply in cells that are located in the paunch. On ordinary trips, they are watered every three or four days, or as often as water is available. Quite appropriately, they possess an extremely keen sense of smell for water, which has proved lifesaving in many instances.

The stupidity and stolidity of the camel is usually mistaken for docility, and it takes very little heed of either kind or harsh treatment. It is able to withstand almost any sort of diet and climate, which is probably the reason for its early domestication, or, more correctly, subjugation. The camel's original home is a matter of uncertainty, so long has it been used to transport man and his goods over burning sands and through bitter cold.

The Bactrian camel of Asia can carry huge loads, as much as 1,000 or 1,500 pounds, though they are seldom loaded to these limits. Baggage camels usually proceed at a pace of two and one-half miles per hour, with passenger dromedaries capable of negotiating as much as a hundred miles per day. To those who are unaccustomed to camel riding, the ride may be quite uncomfortable at first. This is because of the animal's unusual gait, which consists of both feet of the same side being raised and placed forward simultaneously.

OBJECT OF A "NOBLE SPORT"—THE TIGER

An almost exclusively Asiatic creature is the tiger. It ranges as far north as the southern section of Siberia and the Sea of Okhotsk, at the Siberian coast. This northern tiger is larger but less ferocious than the well-known Royal Bengal of India.

The tiger is strictly a carnivorous animal, eating any flesh it is able to strike down. Although tigers will usually flee from an armed man, some of them have gained a reputation as man-eaters,

Courtesy Chicago Park District
THE BENGAL TIGER
This great and powerful feline is hunted from the backs of elephants. It would be suicide to try to hunt it on foot.

Courtesy Chicago Park District

CLOSE-UP OF THE BEWHISKERED SIBERIAN TIGER

Although the tiger's markings and colorings show up rather conspicuously in the zoo cage, in his natural habitat these colorings merge with the surroundings so effectively that hunters have come within yards of him before actually seeing him.

and their depredations have resulted in serious losses of human life. Consequently, tiger hunting has come to be termed a "noble sport," with many governments offering bounties.

The average adult male will grow to about nine and one-half feet in length, and will attain a weight of approximately five hundred pounds. Their strength is attested by the fact that they drag off victims that may weigh two or three hundred pounds.

They wander far and wide during the cold season, but in warm weather they remain in a comparatively small area, usually near water. They hunt and live alone, very rarely traveling in pairs.

Young tiger cubs do not reach maturity until about three years after birth. Consequently, they remain with their mother during this time.

Courtesy Sears Roebuck & Co.

THE WILY AND CUNNING MARTEN

ANIMALS OF NORTHERN EURASIA

THE RUSSIAN BEAR

THE RUSSIAN BEAR is also known as the European brown bear. It has been a familiar sight throughout Europe since before the days of the Roman Empire. At present, besides being found in Russia, it inhabits the Pyrenees mountains, the eastern Alps, Syria, and the Himalayas.

The type thrives well in captivity, and as a result, finds a place in every zoo of importance. Despite the fact that it has been captured for exhibition and hunted for food, it has not been exterminated. It roamed the forests of Great Britain until the twelfth century, but after that time was not to be found there.

The European brown bear is not much different from that type of brown bear found on this continent. The most notable example is the Alaska brown bear. In fact, many zoölogists consider all brown bears to be of the same species, with the differences, if any, being due to mere local variations.

The European brown bears usually grow to a length of about five and one-half feet. Their ordinary span of life is thirty years, although some have attained a much greater age. Their principal foods are berries, fruits, and other vegetation, and the flesh of other animals.

SABLE

The sable is very closely related to the common or pine marten. In fact, it is the most valuable fur-bearer of the weasel family. There are two species, one in Canada, and the other in northern

Courtesy Chicago Park District

THE EUROPEAN BROWN BEAR

Russia and Siberia with which we are concerned. Its very beautiful and highly prized fur is deep brown, with grayish yellow on the throat and sides of the neck. It usually grows to a length of about eighteen inches, exclusive of its tail. The value of its skin ranges from $30 to $200.

It is not an easily captured animal, and traps may not be used lest its pelt be torn and ruined. A sort of pitfall arrangement is employed. The trapping season is from November to January, when the excellence of the fur is at its peak.

Despite the far northern range of its habitat, the sable's fur does not change to a white color in the winter. It makes its home in hollow trees, or it may burrow into the ground. Warmth is assured by lining the nest with leaves, grass, and moss.

THE HAIRY MAMMOTH

Embedded in the frozen soil of northern Siberia have been found perfectly preserved remains of the extinct mammoths that closely resembled the modern elephant of today. There are a few physical differences, however. The mammoth wore a coat of long fur as protection against Arctic blasts, and his great tusks were curved, sometimes almost forming a circle.

Specimens have been found with their tusks and eyes still in their sockets, and their flesh and hair intact. The dogs in exploring parties readily ate the preserved meat. The tusks, which have been an article of commerce for years, grew to huge proportions; the largest ever found were about twelve feet long and weighed about 250 pounds. The stomachs revealed that the mammoth lived on pine cones and shoots that were to be found in prehistoric forests.

The epoch of their existence on the earth has been determined by the drawings found on cave walls in Europe, which revealed that men of the Stone Age hunted these huge mammoths. Their range was not confined to Siberia or Europe, but appears to have been rather wide. The northern section of America has yielded some of their remains.

It has been said that some islands on the coast of Siberia have as their foundations the bones of these once mighty denizens of the world. It is from these islands that most of the ivory is exported, many of the islands consisting of heaps of bones.

REINDEER

The northern regions of forest land in Siberia form the southern limit of range for the wild reindeer found in that country. Most reindeer have been domesticated, but in certain remote parts of the north there are still herds of wild reindeer. As is the case with most other animals, the wild variety grows to a larger size

Courtesy American Museum of Natural History

REINDEER CROSSING A RIVER IN SIBERIA

than the domesticated type. The section to the west, notably
Lapland, depends on the reindeer for existence in that far northern country. The animals are extensively used for drawing sledges
and riding, and as a source of skins for clothing, harness, and
tents. Their flesh and milk are major items of food, and even
their antlers and hoofs find their way into Laplander's lives when
shaped into useful articles.

Reindeer are gregarious by nature, banding together in search
of food. They frequent the mountain tops in summer, and the
valleys in winter. The heat and the insects of the valleys plague
them in the summer time, hence the migration to the mountain
tops; and the wintry blasts make it impossible to remain on the
high hills in cold weather. Even in a domesticated state, there is
still the migratory urge in them and their owners are forced to
make long treks with them in order to satisfy this primal, in-
grained desire to journey.

The reindeer, in common with the other members of the deer
family, is a ruminant that bears antlers. The ruminating animals
are those that chew their cud. The members of the deer family
differ from such ruminants as the cow in that their antlers are

formed of true bone and are solid. The horns of the cow are not of bone and are hollow. The manner in which these animals grow their antlers is curious and interesting. Ordinarily, the old set of antlers falls off during early spring and is replaced by a new set. Two small knobs form on the animal's skull, directly behind the ears, and these are covered with a soft, velvety skin through which the blood courses. Gradually, bony deposits form at the ends of these knobs until, finally, the antlers are completely formed and are covered over with velvet. This velvet is still being fed by the blood and is therefore tender and subject to bleeding if pierced. Later, a ring of bone forms around the base of the antlers and this cuts off the blood supply. When this happens the velvet dries up and that which does not fall off is rubbed off by the animal against trees and rocks. The size of the antlers varies with the age of the animal and some of them have grown as much as fifty inches in length, and possess twenty-five tines.

Of all the species of deer, the Lapland reindeer and the American caribou are the only ones in which both the male and the

Courtesy American Museum of Natural History

IN SIBERIA THE REINDEER IS A "SADDLE HORSE"
Note the wooden saddles and crude panniers.

AMERICAN REIN-
DEER IN LINCOLN
PARK, CHICAGO

Courtesy Chicago Park
District

female grow antlers. The reindeer is also the only species of deer that has been domesticated and put to utilitarian purposes by man.

Reindeer are similar to most of the other members of the deer family except that they are more heavily built, have shorter necks, and more powerful legs which end in hoofs that are widely cloven and splayed so as to facilitate the animal's progress through the deep snows. In the winter time, their coats are naturally heavy and their grayish hair is long and wavy, with a warm growth of under-fur. In the summer, however, they are usually of a dark brown color shading off into white around the nose, the neck, the belly, and the hind-quarters. They stand full-grown about four and a half feet in height and weigh in the neighborhood of four hundred pounds.

Their strength, stamina, and adaptability to frigid climate enable them to travel as much as eight hundred miles in two days, but, ordinarily, they can average ten miles an hour for days and days with loaded sledges.

Reindeer make use of their antlers when fighting among themselves, and many pairs of bucks have been found frozen to death in the snow, their antlers locked in a death embrace. When foraging for food in the snow drifts, they use their antlers, hoofs, and snouts as shovels to push away the snow, so as to get at the green lichen growing beneath.

The wild reindeer of North America, with slightly varying characteristics, are called caribou. In the Arctic regions, in the vicinity of the polar ocean, they are called barren-ground caribou. Reindeer have been transplanted to most of the cold countries of the world but, being frigid temperature animals, they have never thrived farther south than Scotland.

THE LEMMING

The lemming is found scattered through the north, but its particular habitat is on the Scandinavian peninsula. It is a rodent of the mouse family and averages about five inches in size. Its fur is of a yellowish-brown spotted over with black and brown. Its tail is short, its feet are small with five digging claws, and its head is small and round with tiny, beady eyes and small fur-covered ears. It feeds on vegetable matter and burrows under the snow for lichens. It breeds twice a year and brings forth a litter of five young.

The polar lemming turns white in the winter, thus affording it a camouflage which makes it blend in with the snow. Peculiarly, it possesses a set of double claws on one of the forefeet.

When a great horde of lemmings results from extensive breeding, a deep-seated migratory instinct will suddenly cause them to start on a long journey together. Millions of them start on this hegira to nowhere. Nothing stops them. On and on they go blindly, over cultivated fields which they denude completely of growing stuff, through fires which the farmers start to prevent them from over-running their haystacks, granaries and fields, across rivers and over hills, on and on. Following them are usually great crowds of flesh-eating animals and birds which destroy

SWEDISH LEMMINGS

them in prodigious numbers. But, seemingly, their numbers never diminish. Rather, because of their breeding proclivities, they increase and continue until, finally, they reach a high cliff fronting the ocean or its sandy shores. Not even this water deters them. Millions of them fall into the water where they are drowned. As yet, science has not determined the reason for these irregular migrations. One theory, however, states that when the Baltic and North seas were dry land, the lemmings may have made these migrations for feeding purposes. Now, although the land has been filled in with water, the same migratory urge seizes them and they must travel.

SCANDINAVIAN WILD LIFE

In Sweden, the hare, ermine, and weasel are to be found over the entire country. In various sections are squirrels, foxes, wolves and bears, the latter protected by the state because of their growing scarcity. The glutton, wolverine and lynx are restricted to the northern forests. Elk are also protected in this country. The roe deer is found in the South. The badger, otter, and pine marten are quite numerous and are hunted for their skins. Of the birds, the teal, snipe, golden plover and wagtail are scattered over the entire country. The birds, fish and insects are typical of those usually found in north Europe.

In Norway, the bear and the lynx are found. The wolf is quite abundant in Finnmark. Elk are to be found in the eastern forests and in the Trondheim district. Red deer congregate on the west coast, the island of Hitterenx, and in the high fjelds. Foxes, hares, and beavers abound, the latter, however, because they have been growing scarce, being put under protection now. The birds here include the grouse, partridge, migrating ducks, geese and plover, the King eider duck, the Spitzbergen guillemont, the bunting, snowy owl, rough-legged buzzard, the puffin, and the kittiwake.

THE ERMINE, OR WEASEL

Paul's Photos, Chicago

"ANDROCLES," FAMOUS BULL WALRUS OF THE LONDON ZOO

MAMMALS AT THE TOP OF THE WORLD

ANIMAL LIFE IN THE ARCTIC

OLD GEOGRAPHIES have a fascinating way of locating the animals of the world. They show the earth divided into broad weather bands, with the animals of each region resting comfortably on the zone lines, and the great sea beasts half raised from the waters looking curiously at the reader.

Courtesy Chicago Park District

FOUR-YEAR-OLD POLAR BEAR

[189]

At the top of the world, within the Arctic Circle which includes all the ancient ice area to 23½° south of the North Pole, appears the frosty-white polar bear, the animal with the farthest northern range. Slightly below, in the vast land of arctic influence, which in the Western Hemisphere means the region north of tree growth, are pictured the reindeer, caribou, musk-oxen, walrus, seal, whale, sea otter, sea lion, arctic wolf, Eskimo dog, and several small snowland species. Weather conditions are the same around the world within the arctic circle, so the animals north of every country bordering on that zone are similar. This is also true of Antarctica, although there are few animals in the Far South.

The Greeks named the Arctic from the constellation of the Great Bear—Arktos. Beyond the trees—the white birch and the larch grow farthest north—the arctic land becomes a limitless tundra that slopes gently to the arctic sea. On this tundraland the animals live, and here, not at the North Pole, the cold is most severe. The coldest weather ever recorded was -93° F at Verkhoyansk, Siberia. To protect them in unbelievably low temperatures, the northern animals have coats of dense fur.

POLAR BEARS

Because of its thick coat of long, white hair, the polar bear is able to withstand the terrific cold of the arctic winters. It averages in size about ten or eleven feet and has been known to be as large as thirteen feet, weighing as much as sixteen hundred pounds. The feet are black with slightly curved claws. The neck is long, much longer than in other members of the bear family, and is heavily muscled. The head, however, is disproportionately undersized, almost snake-like in appearance.

When the Jackson-Harmsworth Expedition was in Franz Josef Land it had considerable trouble with the many bears there. They had no fear of men, pulled apart partially erected cabins, and ransacked stores of food and implements. One group of them was found sliding down the roof of a snowed-under cabin. They came in such numbers that the men were forced to kill a great many, and they used the flesh for dog-food.

HIND FOOT OF
THE POLAR BEAR.
NOTE THE HAIRY
HEEL

Black Star photo

Despite their enormous weight, they are able to take care of themselves in the water with the ease of a fish. They can swim, dive, roll in the water, and climb icebergs, on some of which they remain for hundreds of miles feeding meanwhile on the seals. Because of their well-padded soles, they can creep noiselessly up to their prey and pounce upon it without making their presence known, biting them and tearing at their flesh with their paws. In catching seals they dive under a floe of ice to come up again in the hole through which the seals originally emerged and around which they are sunning themselves.

Although the polar bear's fur is a silvery white, it also takes on a yellowish color, particularly in captivity. Strangely enough, in spite of the thick covering, polar bears are able to live in zoos in hot countries, and some have been known to withstand the heat better than some tropical animals.

Their devotion to their young cubs is almost humanly maternal. They make every effort to care and provide for them. Unless they are very hungry, or if they mistake him for a seal, they will never attack a man; but if a female finds a man molesting her cubs, the polar bear is the devil incarnate and will fight to the death. They are frolicsome creatures, especially when they are with their young, and for that reason they are great favorites with the children at the zoos.

Courtesy American Museum of Natural History
YOUNG ARCTIC FOX OF NORTHERN CANADA

THE ARCTIC FOX

Foxes are found all over the world, but the arctic fox that lives under the most rigorous and difficult conditions is perhaps the most numerous in a wild state. His range northward almost equals that of the polar bear, and also like the big white bear, the arctic fox seems to feel that the world is uninteresting below the tree line.

The arctic fox is a much smaller animal than the various other foxes and its muzzle and ears are shorter than is usual. During the rigors of arctic winters, it is covered with a thick coat of white fur. As the warm weather approaches, however, it sheds this white fur in patches and takes on a new coat that is gray and brown and sometimes shot through with blue, hence its names of blue fox, stone fox, and pied fox. As winter returns, the summer fur again changes to an almost silvery white. When the pelts are in this color the trappers go after them. Being gregarious and less cunning than most species of fox, arctic foxes are easily trapped. Blue foxes are bred on fox-farms, although their pelts do not bring the high prices of red, silver, and black foxes.

These northern foxes are less wily and suspicious of man than the red and gray foxes, because they have seen fewer trappers.

They continue to live and to raise their young under the most severe conditions. The arctic fox feeds on gulls, geese, mice, lemmings, and hares, all of which are smaller inhabitants of the tundra wastelands.

THE ARCTIC HARE

One of the most northerly penetrating land mammals is the American arctic hare, whose tracks have been found above eighty-three degrees north. It has a total length of twenty-seven inches, and weighs ten to twelve pounds. In summer it is white grizzled with brown, buff, and gray. The tail is white. The face and ears are a tawny-gray with black tips on the ears. In winter, the pelage is white save for the black ear tips. This coloration will sometimes save it from its enemies, the great snowy owl, lynx, weasel, fox, and gerfalcon, all of which prey on it. The arctic hare feeds on lichens and the stunted arctic vegetation. It goes as far south as Hamilton Inlet, Labrador, and west to Hudson Bay.

The Alaska tundra hare is the largest of the arctic hares. It frequents the tundras of northern and northwestern Alaska, from sea-level to two thousand feet elevation. The Greenland hare has a total length of 26.5 inches, a 4.8-inch hind foot and a three-inch ear. Its summer color is whitish with black hairs on back and head. In winter both of these hares are a pure white, except for the black-tipped ears. The Greenland hare ranges through the northwestern coast of Greenland and Ellesmere Land. The Newfoundland hare has a total length of twenty-four inches, and occurs in Newfoundland and Labrador to Hamilton Inlet.

THE MUSK OX—A VANISHING ANIMAL

Qualities of both the ox and the sheep seem present in the strange-looking musk ox which resembles some imaginary prehistoric beast. It stands about five feet at the shoulder, has a large, broad face, and horns that slant down and then turn out and up, like a Spanish mustache. Long, ragged brown hair covers its

Courtesy U. S. Biological Survey
GROUP OF MUSK OXEN IN THE CANADIAN THELON DISTRICT

entire body, but at the shoulders the hair is curly and matted, forming a kind of buffalo hump. Its long, straight body hair conceals its tail. Under this protective outer hair is an under-coat so dense that neither moisture nor cold can penetrate it. The pelt, therefore, is valuable for human wear.

The explorer Stefansson believed the musk ox could be developed into a valuable domestic animal. Its milk is said to be as good as that of the cow, and its flesh is nourishing and full-flavored. Lives of men on two or three arctic expeditions were saved because the Eskimos taught them to eat the musk ox.

The peculiar musk odor of this ox, which does not come from special scent glands, can be smelled at a distance of a hundred yards. Musk oxen once ranged over Alaska, Arctic Canada, and Greenland, but the herds have been so decimated by man that scientists fear the species will soon be extinct. Within the memory of present-day Alaskans the musk-ox herds were found as far west as Point Barrow, the most northerly inhabited part of the

North American continent, but their present range is from the Mackenzie River across the Arctic to Grinnell Land.

The decimation of the musk-ox herds of the Mackenzie Territories was caused partly by the arctic wolf and partly by the high-powered rifles in the hands of northern Indians. Fossil remains show that the musk ox ranged northern Siberia, England, and the plains that are now France and Germany during the Pleistocene period. Then, as now, they were gregarious animals and roved in herds of twenty to thirty in the proportion of about ten cows to one male. The musk ox feeds chiefly on grass, moss and lichens. During the long winter they are forced to subsist on a scanty diet of mosses which they uncover with their hoofs. Young are born in May, normally one calf to each cow, after a nine-month gestation period. Their most dangerous enemy is the wolf. Musk oxen are fleet, so they first try running to escape the wolf packs, but when cornered they form a circle with their sharp horns pointed outward; this defense the wolves can rarely penetrate. The musk-ox is a true arctic animal, hardy and warm-coated. It can survive extreme heat, but when kept in zoos in temperate zones it is sensitive and must be protected from rain and snow.

THE ESKIMO DOG

Erect ears, keen-eyed expression, massive build, and glorious coats of "live" fur—these possessions make the famous Eskimo dog of the north country one of the most beautiful, as well as the most useful, breeds. The Eskimo dog is the animal that draws heavy loads over long trails, that hunts and faces the king of the North, the polar bear, the dog that can "wind" a herd of musk oxen several miles away.

The Eskimo dog is a native of the Arctic, originating in eastern Siberia. He has lived with man for 2,000 years of known history, and is the undisputed leader of the northern dog breeds. Eskimo dogs wear many colors, but the dominant combinations are white bodies with coal-black heads, and all-white bodies with double spinal markings of greyish-silver. If this dog is related to the wolf the association is extremely distant. Like other arctic-land dogs, the Alaskan alamute, Siberian husky, and the Sam-

Courtesy Captain G. Nightingale

A WORLD-FAMOUS DOG TEAM

Six of nine Alaskan sled dogs that made "mushing" history by starting and finishing the longest dog-train trip on record. With Musher "Slim" Williams (left) and "Salvation" Jim Wooler (right) these three-quarter wolf dogs mushed a total of 5,660 miles, from Circle City, Alaska, to the White House, Washington, D. C. The white-faced dog on the extreme right is the famous five-year-old "lead" dog "Rembrandt."

oyede, the Eskimo dog is free of any "doggy" odor. The Eskimo dog's most complete development is in its feet, which are perfect for the trail needs of this hard-working animal. The feet are long, large, and flat, with thick pads studded by stout nails, and luxurious hair cushions between the toes. The thud of these tireless feet is the conventional music of the North.

THE FOOD OF THE ARCTIC FUTURE: THE REINDEER

"Men do not take care of deer, but deer take care of men." This was the old saying the Lapland men announced when they came to Alaska between 1892 and 1902 to teach Eskimos to handle the 1,280 reindeer brought across the Bering Straits from

Siberia during the decade that the Russian government allowed the United States to purchase reindeer.

This original herd has now grown to a million or more reindeer in Alaska, since these valuable food and transport animals double their number every three years. Reindeer offer a perfect source of food in an arctic country, and they have an ability that is most remarkable in a domestic animal: they feed themselves. No matter how severe the weather, it may be 50 or 60 degrees below zero, reindeer locate and dig up their own tundra moss. Tundra moss seems soggy and spongy when stepped on in summer, and in winter the moss remains soft, although it clings to frozen ground. The reindeer tears off the moss and eats snow with it, a combination which, Eskimos believe, produces a flavor the reindeer enjoys. The tundra moss grows slowly, and overgrazed lands will be useless for several years. A fire on the tundra is a major disaster, because the valuable moss requires two decades to grow again.

Reindeer are domesticated caribou, although they seem somewhat unlike the native American caribou of today. They were domesticated many centuries ago by the Lapps and the peoples of northern Siberia, which marked an advance from the hunting

Courtesy American Museum of Natural History

CARIBOU HERD ENGAGED IN "WATCHFUL WAITING"

Courtesy Provincial Information Bureau, Victoria, B. C.
CARIBOU ON THE MOVE IN NORTHERN BRITISH COLUMBIA

stage of civilization to the pastoral. The introduction of reindeer into Alaska, and later into Canada by a world-famous trek, is believed to have advanced present-day Eskimos within a single generation through an entire stage of civilization.

The present wild caribou are the barren ground caribou of Alaska which live in the most desolate Arctic barrens, and a Canadian species called the woodland caribou, which are found south of the timber line. Reindeer owners are careful not to let their tame animals mix with the caribou. Neither reindeer nor caribou are beautiful in the sense of the white-tailed or black-tailed deer. The caribou is rather heavy and short-legged; the reindeer is heavily built, with a short neck and sturdy legs. Both the male and female reindeer grow horns. All varieties of caribou and reindeer have a strong migration urge, and a sincere homing instinct. The spot where a reindeer is born he considers his home, and after making an often purposeless seasonable migration, he longs to return home, although it is usually just a barren spot on the tundra.

THE GREAT FIVE-YEAR REINDEER
TREK ACROSS THE ARCTIC TUNDRA

Beginning on Christmas day in 1929, in the dim light of arctic winter, the Lomen Reindeer Corporation of Alaska, represented by ten experienced deermen, began a trek with a herd of 3,000 reindeer across the top of the Arctic to the delta of the Mackenzie River. The herd had been purchased by the Dominion of Canada to restock the herds depended upon by Eskimos for food. Estimated to last eighteen months, the trek took five years. By map measurement the distance was less than 1,000 miles, but actually the trek was made over unexplored tundras, across impenetrable mountain ranges, and carried through under unfavorable weather conditions. From the time the herd left the starting point it was never again as far south as the Arctic Circle.

When delivery was made to Canada, ninety per cent of the original reindeer herd had been killed by wolves, lost in crevasses, lost by starvation, or killed for food by the herders—but the trek was successful. The real value of the reindeer was proved. Five fawnings had replenished the herd, so the Eskimos had their reindeer.

THE CARNIVORES OF THE SEA

The seals and walruses are the carnivores of the sea. They differ from the terrestrial flesh-eaters in that their feet are fin-like rather than being split into toes. Although much of their time is spent in the water, they are air-breathing mammals.

There are two kinds of seals, earless seals (true seals), and eared seals (fur seals). Most seals are to be found only in the waters of the cold countries of the world. Some are indigenous to only the Arctic and the Antarctic. They have long, glistening bodies, paddle-like fore and hind limbs, and hairy coats that are made waterproof by a fatty secretion from the skin. In the colder climates, the seals have an undergrowth of woolly fur covered over with longer hair in addition to a layer of fat somewhat like the whale's. They are very clumsy on land, moving with their forelimbs and with a sinuous movement of the body motivated by the spine and muscles. But in the water they are marvels of grace, knifing through the water like fish in spite of their enormous weight. Since their diet is chiefly fish, agility in the water is essential for maintaining life. By the action of a sphincter muscle in their nostrils, they are able to close them so that no water can get into the lungs. "Holding their breath," they can remain under water sometimes as long as fifteen minutes.

THE EARLESS SEALS

Although earless seals have no external ears, they nevertheless have the usual internal auditory apparatus. One of the main differences between the eared and earless seals is the fact that the hind flippers of the earless ones stretch out backward, like tails. The Greenland seals can be found not only in Greenland, where they assemble in large numbers, but also along the Atlantic coast from Newfoundland to the Arctic. Most of its six-foot body is a yellowish-white, while the front of the head is black with two broad, black stripes running from the shoulders to the tail, something like a saddle, earning for this particular seal the name of harp or saddleback seal. Immense groups of these animals can be found together, especially in Greenland, where "kills" have been known to reach as high as ten thousand in a single night. The ring seal, a small variety, serves as the main source of food to the Greenland Eskimos, and its skin is used for clothing. The Eskimos wait for the seal to come up to a hole in the ice which it uses for replenishing its air supply, and then they harpoon the beast the moment it shows its sniffing nose.

The leopard seal, another of the earless species, is a denizen of the antarctic wastes; it looks almost like a cat. About twelve feet in length, these seals possess sleek bodies of stiff, silver-gray fur spotted with tufts of dirty-white and yellow-white hair. They feed largely on penguins.

Black Star Photo

ELEPHANT SEAL IN THE HAMBURG ZOO

The Baikal seal is a species of the earless group which frequents, instead of the usual ocean habitats, the inland seas of the Caspian and Lake Baikal.

Aptly and strikingly named is the elephant seal. Largest of the seals, it reaches a length at times of twenty-two feet from its flexible proboscis to its comical tail-flippers. In spite of its size, it is not a particularly dangerous beast. The sealers merely go among a group of them, clout them over the nose with a club, which stuns them, and then proceed to kill them with a slash across the throat. Among themselves, however, when the males fight, they inflict serious damage to each other with their long tusk-like teeth. Because the females never desert their male, the sealers never kill the male until the females have been disposed of. Otherwise, the moment the male is killed, the females would flip-flap their way awkwardly into the ocean. The elephant seal's hide is quite valuable, the hair of the male being blue-gray darkening into brown. They are also taken for the oil which is rendered from their blubber, almost two hundred gallons coming from one animal. At present, because they were killed so promiscuously in the early days, there are only a few left in the world and an elephant seal's fur is considered a rarity.

The elephant seal is not an arctic resident. The "northern" species occurred from Juan Fernandez Island (near Chile) to Lower California. It is now quite rare. The other species lives on the antarctic ice floes and on some of the southern islands near South America.

EARED SEALS

As was explained before, one of the principal differences between the eared and the earless seals is that the eared seals have a definite external ear, while the earless seals do not. Another variation is that the eared seals have hind flippers tipped with rudimentary claws which are turned to the front instead of extending out to the rear like a tail. In this way they are much better able to move on land than the earless variety. In addition, the eared seals have a well-defined neck joining the head to the body. The earless seals have no neck to speak of, the head flowing smoothly into the body. The largest of the eared seals are called sea lions.

THE SEA LION

The largest of the sea lions, the northern species, are found in the waters of the Bering Sea, especially near and on Pribilof Island. These monster seals measure about ten feet in length and about eight feet around in the middle, and weigh well over half a ton. Full-grown, the male's pelt is a honey-brown color with darker shades in spots around the belly and between the front flippers. They can comb this hair with their hind flippers' claws, much like a man running his fingers through his hair. When the breeding season arrives, these seals congregate in great numbers on land where they remain long after their young are born.

Paul's Photos, Chicago
SEA LIONS FROLICKING ON THE COAST OF BRITISH COLUMBIA

THE STELLER
SEA LION

Courtesy American
Museum of Natural
History

Sea lion food consists chiefly of fish and other small denizens of the waters, but when these are scarce they may resort even to sea-weed. The sea lions have an ingenious method of catching sea gulls. Submerging themselves in the water until only the tip of the nose shows, they wait for a bird to swoop down to retrieve what appears to be a tender tid-bit of food floating on the water. Instead of food, when it dives for the morsel, the gull finds the cavernous mouth of the sea lion, which calmly proceeds to gulp it down.

One need not stalk sea lions. They can be heard from some distance away. The old bull sea lion bellows constantly, almost like a bull, while the younger ones bleat in concert. A group of them on an island sounds like a stockyard killing pen.

There are four other species of sea lions in addition to the one described. One species lives in Patagonia. The commonest species in captivity is the California species. These animals are well known for their rather intelligent behavior.

ELEPHANT SEAL
WAITING FOR A
BITE OF SUPPER

Black Star Photo

A FEMALE FUR
SEAL STANDING
GUARD

Courtesy American
Museum of Natural
History

FUR SEALS

The northern fur seal, commonly known as the sea bear, can also be found in the Bering Sea. It is from this species of seal that most of the seal pelts for making fur coats are derived. The underfur of these animals is soft and luxurious, with longer hairs that are taken out by shaving the flesh-side of the pelt, which contains the roots of these longer hairs. Full grown, the male of this species reaches a size of six feet with a weight of six hundred pounds. The female, however, runs smaller, attaining the weight at times of only eighty pounds, and the length of about four feet.

In the latter part of May, the male seals repair to Kamchatka, to certain islands in the Bering Sea, and especially to Pribilof Islands. There they seem to stake out a claim of their own. After a time, the female seals arrive and a general fight starts among the males for possession of as many females as each of them can garner, some males acquiring as many as forty. The fights continue while each male tries to win additional females for himself. Finally, in August, after the seal calves have been born and weaned and taught to swim by their mothers, the colony breaks up and they all slide off the islands into the sea. The amazing thing about these breeding months is that during the entire period the male does not partake of food, his sustenance being drawn from the reserve fat that he has stored in his blubber.

THE WALRUS

Although in outward appearance the walrus, or sea horse, resembles a seal, it can be put into a category all its own. One difference between the two animals is that the walrus has a hairy "mustache" on its projecting nose. Also, it possesses a pair of tusks, outgrowths of the two upper canine teeth, which are formidable-looking objects. The walrus uses these tusks for digging into the sand for shellfish and other edibles and also for swinging itself from the water onto an ice floe. Although not possessing external ears, it turns its front flippers outward, like the eared seal.

At one time the walrus could be found considerably farther south, but now it is confined practically to the Arctic. When full grown they average about twelve feet in length, but some of them have been known to be as much as twenty feet long. From the reports of some ancient travelers, some had been sighted which were claimed to have reached almost elephantine proportions. The average weight is about two thousand pounds. There is usually a sparse growth of hair over the black wrinkled skin of the walrus except in old age, when the hair falls out.

To the Eskimo, the walrus is a valuable source of sustenance. Oil rendered from its blubber is eaten by them together with the

Courtesy American Museum of Natural History

A BULL WALRUS

flesh. Its tusks are fashioned into fish hooks and tips for their harpoons, while fish nets and ropes are made of its intestines. At one time, immense herds of walruses tumbled over each other, bellowing and sporting on the various Arctic islands. But ever since industry received a setback, these enormous herds have been attacked. In the first ten years of this massacre, it is said that more than one hundred thousand were killed, netting the hunters about four hundred thousand pounds of tusk ivory and about two million gallons of oil. However, man is not the only enemy of the walrus. Polar bears attack them quite often and, when aroused, the ordinarily peaceful walrus can be galvanized into a dangerous mountain of flesh with two terrible effective tusks as weapons. A herd of walruses has been known to attack a marauding polar bear and tear it to bits.

A young walrus starts to develop its tusks only after it is two years old. Until that time it cannot forage for itself and must necessarily depend upon its mother for food, continuing to suckle until it is approximately the size of its mother. During this time, human-like, the walrus dam holds its young in its front flippers. When its young is endangered, the mother walrus will fight desperately to protect it.

SEA OTTERS

Eskimos who have hunted the sea otter for many generations say they have never heard of a sea otter pup's being born on land. Sea otters are creatures of the open sea. Originally, they swam in the waters of the whole world, but their pelts are so valuable they have been sought for centuries by man, and the otters have retreated to the *bad* waters and treacherous reefs and rocks of the polar seas.

Sea otters have long, rubber-like bodies, bulldog heads, whiskers, and ears that close when the animal submerges. When the otter is on land these ears are fully open, because his hearing is highly developed and is his chief protection against enemies.

One of the sea otter's charms is his love of play. Otters kept as pets have developed an insatiable desire to romp and show affection for their owners. In their natural state, otters find snow slides that lead into water and slide until exhausted. Otters in a zoo are comforted when they are given a sliding board. Sea bears and sea lions are the sea otter's natural enemies.

AN INDUSTRY 1,000 YEARS OLD

Sailing with a whaling fleet in Baffin Bay, or one of the other great whale regions of the northern seas, is an adventure which scientists believe will vanish before the close of the present century. Commercial whaling has attracted man for a thousand years. The returns in oil, whalebone, ivory, and ambergris were almost as great as gold—and certainly more dependable. But the value of the whale has encouraged careless slaughter, and the whale has not replaced itself, because, like all large animals, it is a slow breeder.

Probably the largest animal that ever lived, including the enor-

Pauls Photos, Chicago
WHALING IN THE NORTHWEST
Note the thickness of the blubber being cut from the carcass.

mous extinct dinosaurs, is the blue or sulphur-bottom whale, which has been found to measure over 100 feet in length and weigh 150 tons or more. The strength of the blue whale, estimated by its ability to tow whaling ships, is incredible.

Although it spends all of its time in the water and outwardly resembles a fish, the whale is, nevertheless, a genuine mammal in that it bears its young alive and nurses them. Whales do not have gills for taking oxygen out of the water, so they cannot breathe while submerged and hence cannot remain under water for any length of time. When it is finally compelled to rise to the surface, the whale blows a stream of vapor and water twenty feet into the air through a "spout," which issues from nostrils on the upper part of its head called "blow-holes." Then it takes in a fresh supply of air for another submersion. However, this air does not make the whale buoyant and prevent it from sinking below surface. Very little is known about his respiration. Before

Paul's Photos Chicago

AN OCEAN MONSTER WASHED ASHORE OFF VANCOUVER,
BRITISH COLUMBIA

diving, he probably ventilates his lungs well and then fills them
with as much air as possible. Only when the oxygen is depleted
does the whale rise to the surface, spout, and take in another supply of oxygen to mingle with its blood. Contrary to popular
belief, the whale does not blow up water through its "blow-hole."
It ejects a stream of warm air which, when it comes in contact
with the cold air, vaporizes. If the whale's head is deep in the
water, some water naturally is shot up with the hot air which
accounts for the misconception.

Although there are several species of whales, they are very
similar in external characteristics. Typical of all of them is the
large head which, in some cases, constitutes almost a third of the
entire length of the whale. All have forelimbs which resemble a
fish's fins, but these are really five-fingered hands with a web covering, so that the animal can keep on an even keel and also hold

its young when nursing. Its propelling agency is in the form of
a horizontal tail. Although whales are hairless, some of them show
traces of hair in the embryonic stage, a remnant of their mam-
malian heritage. Beneath their thick hides is a layer of resilient
fat, or blubber, two feet thick, which serves to keep the animal
warm and also forms a protective shell for the inner organs
against the immense weight of water.

There are two separate orders of whales. The toothed whales
comprise one order and are characterized by the presence of teeth
in one or both jaws and by the possession of only one "blow hole."
The whalebone whales, on the other hand, are toothless and bear
plates of baleen, or whalebone, in the mouth. Baleen is, in reality,
not bone, but a horny material. When the whale feeds, it opens
its cavernous mouth and takes in great gulps of water that are
teeming with minute animals of almost microscopic size. When
it closes its mouth, the water is strained out by the baleen as the
tongue is raised and pressed against it. The animals that remain
are then swallowed. The fact that such an enormous beast can
subsist on minute animal-life is amazing; but even more amazing
is the size of this whale's throat, which is so small that if a whale
tried to swallow even a small mackerel, it might choke to death.

WHALEBONE WHALES

The "right" whale is also known as the northern whale and
the Greenland whale. Its habitat is the icy waters of the Arctic
Ocean. Its head is enormous, with a mouth fifteen feet long, six
feet wide, and ten feet high. Inside this mouth are a few hundred
rows of baleen strips, hanging from the upper jaw like hair, and
weighing about two thousand pounds in themselves.

Found in practically every ocean except the Antarctic, the
rorqual whale, also known as the finback whale and fin whale, is
one of the most numerous of the whales. Certain species of the
rorqual vary in size, the lesser fin whale averaging about thirty
feet while Sibbald's fin whale occasionally reaches a length of
about eighty-five feet. The common rorqual is seldom larger
than seventy feet, although occasional catches have been much
larger. When one realizes that whales of this type average seventy

or eighty tons in weight, it should be quite easy to visualize the immense bulk of these leviathans of the seas.

Because its blubber is not as thick as that of most whales and because its baleen is sparse and of inferior quality, the rorqual is not as desirable as other whales to whalemen. It is, however, a ferocious fighter, and this may also account in part for the whalemen's aversion to it. There is a record of one harpooned rorqual that dragged a boatload of whalemen to their death under a floe of ice. Unlike that of the Greenland whale, its gullet is not undersized and it can accommodate hundreds of pounds of fish at a gulp. One captured rorqual's stomach was found to contain more than six hundred large codfish together with a number of other large fish. When it forages close to the shore for schools of fish, it is sometimes left stranded high and dry on the shore.

The humpback whale is about fifty feet in length and is distinguished by its possession of a distinct hump and a series of fluted folds on its throat. These invite more than the usual number of barnacles that attach themselves to most whales.

TOOTHED WHALES

The massive sperm whale of arctic waters, like the others of this group, retains its teeth all its life. Unlike the "right" whale, which has a tiny throat and eats only small animals, the sperm whale has an expansive throat and eats huge squids at one gulp. From the oil of the sperm is reduced a substance called spermaceti, used in the manufacture of cosmetics; but its most valuable product is ambergris—the precious substance that is sold to perfume manufacturers for fabulous sums, and is the true pot of gold at the end of ocean rainbows. The ambergris is not made into perfume, but it is the fixative that holds the expensive essential oils and makes perfume odors lasting.

One of the strangest of these whales is the narwhal, which also frequents the arctic waters. It differs from the ordinary whale in that it is smaller, seldom measuring over fifteen feet in length, and that its head is not as bulky. It has teeth in both jaws, but in its upper jaw are two tusklike teeth which project beyond the other teeth and are hollow. In the female of the species, these tusks are of ordinary length. But in the male, the left tusk grows into a long, spiraled, ivory spear that juts out in front of the head for eight or nine feet. The exact purpose of this formidable weapon is undetermined as yet. Some authorities say that it is used to bore breathing holes through the ice when the narwhal is imprisoned under solid ice. Others claim that its development has been brought about by the fact that the narwhal males fight for their females, much as do reindeer, and use their developed tusks for combative purposes. At times, some narwhals have been found with two spears growing from their heads, but these have been rare and a right tusk is almost non-existent. Whale oil obtained from the narwhal is much finer than that of most whales, and, although it is a smaller catch than the usual whale, the narwhal is sought for its oil and its ivory.

The beluga or white whale ranges mostly in the Arctic seas, although it occasionally wanders down into the warmer waters. It runs in size to about sixteen feet and is called the white whale because it is almost the color of cream. Unlike most whales, it sometimes leaves its feeding grounds in the ocean to swim up rivers for salmon. The Eskimos consider its flesh highly palatable and "jerk" it in the summer for winter consumption. Its hide

Courtesy American Museum of Natural History

FINBACK WHALE HARPOONED OFF NORWEGIAN COAST

furnishes a fine, soft leather when tanned. The oil rendered from its blubber is finer and more desirable than ordinary whale oil.

A number of other species of whales frequent the waters of the Arctic and the north Atlantic, around the Scandinavian peninsula, Greenland, and Iceland. These vary only in small particulars and therefore require no extended treatment. Among them may be mentioned the bottle-nose whale, which has a nose that, in some respects, really does resemble a bottle.

THE PORPOISE

The porpoise, a miniature toothed whale, ranges the north Atlantic Swedish waters; it is the only species of whale in the Baltic Sea and also in the north Pacific Ocean. In size it averages between five and seven feet. The upper surfaces of its body are a deep black, almost blue-black, while its belly is white with a sheen of silver. Gregarious, the porpoise travels in schools. A group of them, with teeth in each jaw, can almost deplete the waters of a district of all its fish. A school can easily be recognized because of the distinctive back-fins which flash through the water as the porpoises frolic in groups, playing a game almost like "follow the leader" in a line that sometimes extends a mile in length.

CANADIAN ANIMALS

THE MOOSE

THE LARGEST OF THE DEER FAMILY, living or extinct, is the moose. It ranges through the forests of Nova Scotia, New Brunswick, Ontario, Winnipeg, Minnesota, Wyoming and Yellowstone Park, British Columbia, Yukon, and Alaska. The moose is related to the European elk which inhabits the northern parts of Norway, Sweden, Finland, and the northwestern Soviet Republic. The American elk is incorrectly named. The most impressive aspect of the moose is the size. Its height at the shoulders averages about six feet, and the total length of its head and body is about eight feet six inches. The spread of the antlers is fifty-two to fifty-eight inches. The largest antlers now in the Field Museum of Natural History, Chicago, came from the Kenai Peninsula in Alaska. They have a spread of seventy-eight and one-half inches and the greatest width of the flattened part termed palmation is sixteen inches. There are thirty-four points to the antlers which, with the dry skull, weigh ninety-three pounds. That is a stupendous weight for an active animal to carry on his shoulders. The female has no antlers.

The forelegs of the moose are about four feet in length, the hind ones somewhat shorter. Largely owing to this, moose do not run like other deer, but cover the ground with great strides. Sometimes, when rushing along, the legs are worked like stilts, the hind ones being spread to straddle the front ones without striking them, the long, pointed, cloven hoofs clattering noisily. When a large tree trunk is encountered the moose merely steps over it, without materially slackening its speed.

Courtesy National Parks of Canada

BULL MOOSE IN ELK ISLAND PARK, ALBERTA, CANADA

The moose has a short, thick neck which coupled with its long forelegs, makes grazing difficult. To reach succulent marsh grass it has to kneel on its front legs. Its broad, square, flexible nose, which overhangs like a proboscis, solves some of its dietary problems, since it is used, together with the tongue, to pluck twigs and aquatic plant stems. The nostrils are large and the sense of smell is well developed. The ears are large and pointed. The throat has a hanging extension of skin and long hair called "the bell." In older animals this becomes pouch-like, and may grow a foot in length. A high hump adorns the shoulder. The tail is short, almost rudimentary. The coarse hair is three to six inches long. The males and females are the same color, the upper coat being blackish-brown to black in winter, and the lower belly and legs a pale brownish-gray. The muzzle and face show some gray. In summer the color lightens somewhat, the legs becoming a tawny-gray. The young are of a reddish-brown color.

Moose dwell only in forested areas, preferring the vicinity of lakes and ponds where aquatic plants supplement their diet. They eat not only water lilies, but will dive, if necessary, to loosen the tender bulbous roots. As a rule their long legs enable them to forage for aquatic plants with ease. The moose are powerful swimmers and do not hesitate to cross a lake several miles wide to find a new feeding range. Moose browse on the stems and leaves of hemlock, spruce, aspen, willow, balsam, birch, juniper, maple, and alder trees. By bearing down saplings between their legs, they ride along them and thus reach the upper branches. The long legs assist further when the moose rears upward to peel young bark or to reach tender twigs.

HABITS OF THE "WOOD-EATER"

With the advent of November, moose seek their winter quarters. Here they must have an abundant supply of their favorite trees, together with mosses and lichens growing on or about them. They even eat the green wood, hence the Indian names, Musu or Mooswa, meaning "wood-eater." When the snow falls, the moose, by constant travel from tree to tree in an area of some acres makes paths which are trampled down. This maze of trails is called a "moose yard," where several families may dwell for mutual protection. It is only in winter that the moose is in danger from carnivorous animals. Should the deep snow freeze over, the animal will have difficulty in traveling. If this happens, a lone moose, however powerful, will easily fall a victim to a band of timber wolves, a pair of cougars or bears. When in the forest, the moose arches his antlers back and breaks through the densest growth. In spring, the antlers fall off, and a new pair is developed.

The mating season is in the fall, when the bull moose, with full-grown antlers, seeks his cow. Usually a timid and retiring animal, it is now bold, and may even charge a human being. It sounds a loud roar that, at times, may be heard two or three miles away. Again, it challenges other rivals by clashing its antlers against trees. In one fight between powerful, evenly matched bull moose, they butted each other fiercely. The impact caused them to rebound. At a second onslaught the antlers held and the con-

Courtesy National Parks of Canada

A PAIR OF MOOSE TWINS IN RIDING NATIONAL PARK, MANITOBA, CANADA

testants coursed about until one brushed against a tree with his hind quarters. This gave an opening to his antagonist, who shifted his antlers against the victim's neck. He then pierced the region behind the shoulder, and finally gored him in the side. After seeing the death of the vanquished, the victor left, accompanied by the cow moose, which had quietly watched the combat. In this season the bull moose, if wounded or cornered by a hunter, may charge his tormentor and mangle or kill him. In early spring the cow moose separates from her mate, and retires, preferably to some island, where one or two calves are born in May. The calves usually stay with the cow for two years. At fifteen months a moose may be five feet high, five feet nine inches long, and weigh three hundred pounds. A full-grown bull moose will weigh one thousand to fourteen hundred pounds. The average length of life of a moose is from fifteen to twenty years.

In northern Minnesota there is a national preserve containing over ten thousand moose. New Brunswick also has a great moose and caribou preserve. On the protected Kenai peninsula, Alaska, roam the Alaska moose, which average larger than the common moose, and weigh up to eighteen hundred pounds.

When taken as calves in Canada and in Sweden, moose have been trained to draw sleighs and to labor like horses. However, any unconfined pet moose with mature antlers is a potential menace.

Black Star Photo

CANADIAN WOODLAND CARIBOU

THE LYNX—TIMID WILD CAT OF CANADA

The Canada lynx is widely distributed, ranging from Pennsylvania to 60° north latitude, across the continent, and from Alaska into Oregon and the Colorado Rockies. The erect, sharply pointed and black tufted ears, bobbed unringed tail and long legs with large, hairy paws characterize the lynx. Male lynxes are thirty-six to thirty-nine inches long, including a four-inch tail. A full-grown lynx is about eighteen inches high and has a hind foot more than nine inches long; it possesses twenty-eight sharp teeth and strong sharp, retractile claws. About its throat is a coat of ruff, and the usual protective guardhairs adorn his upper lip. The ruff is usually parted at the chin, making a divided beard, adorned with black bars. The upper parts of the animal are of a grizzled gray, brown, and blackish color, while its belly and throat are grayish-white with touches of brown and blackish color. The tail is tipped with black. In early summer, the hair is browner than usually, but in the late summer a buff color predominates. A mature animal weighs twenty to twenty-

Courtesy New York Zoological Society
YOUNG LYNX FINDS LIFE IN THE ZOO UNEXCITING

five pounds; the record is forty-four pounds. The female is smaller than the male.

French-Canadians call the lynx "lucivée" or *loup cervier*, which means deer-wolf, a probable reference to the old superstition of the existence of werewolves. In the Middle Ages people believed that some individuals could, by supernatural means or through their own efforts, transform themselves into wolves in shape and appetite, and it is said that this belief still persists. Some regard the lynx as a deer killer, desirous of sucking its blood. Unlike the house cat, the lynx swims fearlessly.

It does its hunting chiefly at night. Crouching, flattened on a limb, like a panther, it is ready to leap upon its prey. It eats birds, snakes, frogs, but it particularly relishes small mammals, such as rabbits, hares, squirrels, mice, and muskrats. Lynxes have been known to kill foxes, goats, sheep, mountain sheep, and small deer.

In the winter, it runs along the top of the snow; its broad feet do not break through the crust. In Canada at this season it

Courtesy U. S. Biological Survey

THIS BAY LYNX IS TAKING LIFE EASY AFTER A FINE BIG MEAL
OF PARTRIDGE OR RABBIT

is easy for the lynx to capture the abundant large hares. Oddly enough, though the lynx looks fierce, it is quite timid. Indians of the Mackenzie region snare the animal with a rope noose at the entrance of a brush enclosure, using beaver musk for bait. The flesh is eaten with relish by Indians and by some of the whites as well. When a lynx goes a-wooing, its yowl and caterwaul are those of the house cat magnified many times.

The lynx is born in litters of from two to four kittens between April and July, in a lair hidden away in the brush. If a lynx kitten is captured young enough, it can be readily tamed as a house pet.

The arctic lynx is browner in color than the Canada lynx and has a very thick fur. It ranges from Point Barrow, Alaska, to British Columbia. Males average forty-one inches long, with a five-inch tail. The largest lynx ever found was fifty inches in length. The Newfoundland lynx has a darker and richer looking fur than the Canada lynx.

Courtesy Yosemite National Park

CALIFORNIAN WILDCAT ON THE HUNT

THE WILD CAT

The bay lynx, variously called bobcat, red lynx, or wild cat, is the typical member of the rufus group of lynx. It courses through North America from southern Canada to Georgia, and westward as far as Montana. In general, it resembles the Canadian lynx, but the feet are smaller, the ears are set at about forty-five degrees and are but slightly black-tufted, the tail is longer and rather bushy and is not black all around at the tip. The average length is thirty-six inches; the tail length is about seven inches; the hind foot, seven inches. The bay lynx weighs about twenty pounds. Exceptional bay lynxes are fully as large as the largest arctic lynx.

The under fur is brownish, yellowish or reddish and is spotted. The hair is shorter than that of the Canadian lynx. The upper parts are brown and buff and spotted with brownish-black or

Courtesy J. Bradford Pengelly

PAIR OF CATS BROUGHT FROM THE ISLAND OF CRETE
Cretan Cats are direct descendants of the Egyptian wild cats.

black and are darkest on the back. The sides are lighter and have more yellow. The tail above is like the back, but below it is light and has a whitish tip. The belly is yellowish-white with black spots, and the breast is whitish with black bars. The bay lynx, like the Canadian lynx, wears a ruff, but his is smaller than that of his relative. He has two white bars on each cheek.

Wild cats dwell in wooded or mountainous areas and even in desert regions. Two to four kittens are born in a litter, in April or May. The food of the wild cat is birds and small mammals. If a farm is in reach of the lair, the wild cat may seize small pigs, lambs, turkeys, or small poultry. Most of their hunting is done at night. Wild cats live to be about six years old.

There are about ten species of wild cats in North America. The Florida bobcat is thirty-nine inches long and is dark in color, while the Texas bobcat is chestnut brown above. The California bobcat, reddish-brown and blackish above, is thirty-four inches long. The desert bobcat is thirty-seven inches long and lives in desert parts of California. The mountain bobcat is forty-one inches long and is found in Wyoming, Colorado, Utah, and New Mexico. The Nova Scotia or giant bobcat is forty inches long and is decidedly heavier than other wild cats. Its upper parts are brownish, with black and gray.

The house cat is descended from the Egyptian wild cat. It seems to have been first tamed to keep mice from grain stores. The word "puss" is apparently derived from the name of the Egyptian moon goddess Pasht, patroness of the sacred cats. The trading Phoenicians introduced the Egyptian cats into Europe.

In recent years many litters of domesticated kittens have been dumped in outlying areas. Such animals will mature in the wild state and become predatory. Many female cats bearing engraved collars have been found with their wild young. The ears of some of these collared cats had reverted to the long-haired, tufted type of wild cat. Game birds which had been introduced were exterminated and numerous heads and wings of songbirds attested to the skill of the cats which had once more become "wild cats."

FOXES OF MANY KINDS

From times immemorial the red fox has been considered one of the most cunning of animals. This belief originated the custom of calling a sly person "foxy." Through the literature of all countries are found tales of fox hunts and of the fox eluding the hounds. The red fox is superior to the gray fox in speed and in cunning, and has been found to run at a speed of about thirty miles an hour.

The eastern red fox inhabits the northeastern United States. Its total length is forty-one inches of which sixteen inches comprise the tail. The nose is long and tapering, and the long, erect ears are pointed. Its body is slender like that of a small dog. The tail is long and bushy and has a white tip. The golden-yellow fur is long and soft. Its head is reddish-yellow, grizzled with white. The front of the legs is mostly blackish-brown. The female is about one-tenth smaller than her mate. From four to nine cubs

Courtesy U. S. Forest Service

BLACK FOX RANCHING IN ALASKA

Courtesy U. S. Biological Survey

MATURE SILVER FOX

YOUNG FOX ON THE PROWL
FOR MICE

are born in April. The food consists of birds and such mammals as mice, squirrels, hares, and rabbits. In turn, the fox must avoid eagles, great horned owls, wolves, lynxes, and other carnivora. The fox may live to be ten years old.

A good fox skin is worth about ten dollars. Occasionally sport or phase colors occur in a red fox litter, the pelage in rare cases becoming black, with a tail also black, except for the white tip. Such a fox is called a black fox, silver grey fox, or silver fox. The latter has white-tipped hairs. Five skins have been sold for as high as four thousand dollars. Many fox farms have been established for commercial production of fur. The record price for a pair of guaranteed breeders was forty thousand dollars. Another color phase is the cross fox, which has a black muzzle, black legs, and black under parts. The black tail has a white tip. The body is reddish-yellow to steel gray and bears a dark band across the shoulders and another dark band running down the middle of the back, making a dark cross. It is found from New York to Manitoba. A good cross skin is worth twenty dollars or more. All three phases may occur in the same litter.

The Nova Scotia red fox is larger and darker than the eastern red fox, and is about forty-three inches long. The Kodiak red fox is fifty-two inches, including an eighteen-inch tail, and is found on Kodiak Island. It is the largest of the twelve species.

The gray fox, or tree fox, ranges from the Mississippi Valley to the Atlantic Ocean, southwest to Texas, and along the Pacific coast and in Wyoming. There are about twelve species that are from twenty-eight to forty-two inches long over all. They climb trees when pursued by hounds. They eat small mammals, birds, fish, reptiles, acorns, and berries. The kit fox lives on the plains from Colorado and Nebraska to Saskatchewan. It resembles the red fox, but is smaller. The arctic fox has already been described elsewhere in this volume.

MARTENS

The American marten, also called pine marten or American sable, is related to the weasel. In length it is twenty-five inches, including an eight-inch tail, and has a hind foot that exceeds three inches. It roams the forests from Virginia to the Rockies, and north to Labrador. It has a sharp-pointed nose like a fox. The body is yellowish-brown with blackish-brown on the back. It feeds on small mammals, grouse, reptiles, and berries. Besides man, its chief enemies are the fisher marten, lynx, and great horned owl.

The Labrador marten is twenty-seven inches in total length and is a dark brown to blackish. It roves northeast Labrador and Ungava Bay to Belle Isle Strait. The Newfoundland marten has a deep chocolate color. The female is twenty-two inches in total length. From three to four young are born in April. The skin is highly prized in the fur market.

Pennant's marten, variously called fisher, pekan, black fox, or black cat, is the largest marten. In length it is thirty-eight inches, including a fourteen-inch tail, and weighs twelve to eighteen pounds. It occurs from Maine north to James Bay in Quebec, west through Manitoba up to sixty degrees north latitude, onward to the Pacific, and south to Wyoming. In general, it resembles

Courtesy U. S. Biological Survey

A YOUNG PINE MARTEN

Courtesy Sears Roebuck & Co.

FULL-GROWN PEKAN, OR FISHER

the American marten, but has a blunter muzzle. The fur is gray-ish-brown to brownish-black and is a dark brown on chest and belly. The fisher marten eats small mammals, birds, and also fish when it can steal them. It even turns porcupines over to eat the underside. The rabbit is easily worn down when pursued by the fisher. About three young are born in May, usually in a hollow-tree nest, thirty to forty feet from the ground. The fisher is a fierce fighter and is said to be able to kill the fox, raccoon, and lynx. It pursues and eats its relative, the American marten. Like the wolverine, it often devours trapped animals.

The Pacific fisher is found in the forests from northern California to Alaska. The total length is forty-two inches with a tail length of fourteen inches.

WOLVERINE—BANDIT OF THE FORESTS

The wolverine is the owner of another name, and it is one that is quite appropriate—the "Glutton." The latter name is derived from the attitudes it displays, namely, sullenness, greed, and extreme cunning. Its methodic springing of traps and stealing of bait provide trappers with many periods of exasperation. The food obtained in this and other ways is gulped down in choking sizes.

Its ordinary food supply consists of almost any animal or bird it can kill. Consequently, sick or injured deer are often killed by this bandit of the forests. Its inclination to steal is so pronounced that it often carries away and hides articles of no possible use to it.

Built somewhat on the order of a small bear, the wolverine usually attains a length of about thirty-six inches, and a weight of twenty-five pounds.

The wolverine belongs to the weasel family, which is usually a fierce and bloodthirsty tribe. It might well be called the king of its family, because it is the largest member and certainly does not possess a more placid disposition than any of its relatives.

Its reputation is also blackened by the fact that it will not attack larger animals, but does not hesitate to make a meal of one

Courtesy New York Zoological Society
A MATURE WOLVERINE
More plentiful in Canada than in the United States. More than 150,000 wolverines are marketed in Canada yearly.

that has been previously killed. The animals it will attack are those it is almost certain of conquering.

Despite its size and ungainly appearance, it can cover ground fairly rapidly when pressed, and can ascend trees with comparative ease when food is the goal.

THE OTTER

Otters are related to weasels and minks, but differ in being larger, in having webbed feet, and in not having musk or scent glands so well developed.

The Canada otter is from forty to forty-five inches over-all, the tail being twelve and one-half to fifteen inches long. The hind foot is about four inches long. The limbs are five-toed and webbed, the forelegs being larger and heavier. The head is broad and flat, has strong jaws and long, bristling guard-whiskers, and contains thirty-six stout, sharp teeth. The small black eyes have a special membrane beneath the lower eyelids which can cover the eyeballs. Its small pointed ears are closable. The black nose is

Paul's Photos Chicago

OTTER ENJOYING A QUIET BREAKFAST

short and the cheeks and chin are a brownish gray. The tail, heavy and flat at its base, tapers to a point. In addition to a muscular, sinuous body, the otter has a powerful tail and legs which make it possible for it to adapt itself to a semi-aquatic life and diet. Its fur is a dark, glossy brown, paler in hue below. The long, shiny outer hair covers a short, thick, and soft underfur.

The otter swims horizontally, darting down after any fish it sees, dodging back and forth until it corners its prey and finally drags it ashore to its den to be devoured. Grasping the fish in its forepaws, the otter bolts its victim head first leaving only the tail.

Though otters usually live in pairs, half a dozen of them sometimes occupy a single burrow. These burrows, which are dug in such a way that they have several entrances, one of which is usually under water, are located near the banks of a lake or stream, or on the seashore—wherever fish are plentiful. For sustenance, the otter enjoys eating frogs, crayfish, clams, mussels, and other mollusks. Often they attack smaller mammals such as muskrats and young beaver. In winter the otters may be forced to migrate to far-distant rapids or waterfalls in order to find open water where they can fish. In case of winter near-famine, otters may prey on wild or domestic fowl or their eggs.

To escape capture, otters will slide along the snow or dive into deep snow and burrow far enough to elude the pursuer, whether wild beast or human. No ordinary dog can whip an otter on land, and in water, the otter is greatly the superior. To protect fishing streams from the depredations of otter, a special breed of dogs called the otter hound is trained to fight the otter even in its water den. The otter hound has powerful jaws, good teeth, and a rough, oily, woolly fur that withstands the cold water and the otter's sharp teeth. It is about twenty-five inches high and weighs from fifty to seventy-five pounds.

A litter of otters consists of from one to three young otters, born in late April, and remaining with the mother until winter. Both old and young otters enjoy playing in a grassy field or on snowbanks. The noted naturalist John James Audubon thus describes otters disporting themselves on a clay bank: "The otters ascend the bank at a place suitable for their diversion, and some-times where it is very steep, so that they are obliged to make an effort to gain the top. They slide down in rapid succession where there are many at a sliding place. On one occasion we were resting on the bank of Canoe Creek, a small stream near Henderson, which empties into the Ohio, when a pair of otters made their appearance, and not observing our proximity, began to enjoy their sliding pastime. They glided down the soapy-like muddy surface of the slide with the rapidity of an arrow from a bow, and we counted each one making twenty-two slides before we disturbed their sportive occupation." Sometimes otters cast themselves down on the breast and belly, with forelegs bent upward, and thus coast down an icy snowbank into the water or along the pond ice.

In India and southeastern Asia, the otter is tamed sufficiently to fish for its master. Held by a collar and long line, it returns with the fish to the boat. Otters are sometimes tamed as pets, be-coming friendly like a dog.

The Canada otter occurs from Labrador to Alaska and Yukon, and south to Washington, also on the Atlantic coast as far south as South Carolina. The otter of the interior, fifty-three inches over-all, is found in Nebraska and has a dark reddish-brown summer coat. The Florida otter, totaling fifty-one inches, has a chestnut-brown upper coat. The Pacific otter, forty-five inches in total length, is distinguished by a seventeen-inch tail, the upper parts being a reddish-brown. Becoming paler below, it has head, neck and breast of pale brown. It frequents the Pacific region from Alaska to Oregon. The Newfoundland otter has a total length of forty inches, with a fourteen-inch tail. The upper parts are brown to blackish. It is lighter on the neck and sides of the head. The life span of the otter is from ten to twelve years.

CANADIAN OTTERS ON THE RUN

ANIMALS OF THE ROCKY MOUNTAINS
AND WESTERN UNITED STATES

S O FAR AS CLIMATE, relief, elevation and flora are concerned, the western section of North America is a region of startling contrasts. The region includes mountain peaks, snow-covered the year round, and valleys where snow is never seen; the rain-drenched forests of the northwest coast and the deserts of the southwest, where any form of precipitation is scarcely known; from Death Valley, two hundred seventy-six feet below sea-level, to mountain tops that stretch skyward for a distance of more than fourteen thousand feet.

As a result of this varied environment there are a great number of different kinds of animals in this region. Also, because much of the area is unsuited for human settlement the number of animals that live there is very large. Another reason for the large number of animals is that the United States and the Canadian governments have established game preserves here. These refuges consist of spots where animals may live the year round without fear of being molested by hunters. One of the most famous of these places in the United States is Yellowstone Park.

In this vast region there live animals as varied as the bison, the largest North American mammal; the bear, largest carnivorous beast on the continent; the tiny pine squirrel, and the pika, or "crying hare."

Courtesy National Parks of Canada

BISON BULL AT WAINWRIGHT, ALBERTA

THE HOOFED ANIMALS

One of the largest groups in the northwestern section of North America is the hoofed animals which include bison, sheep, goats, pronghorned antelopes, deer, and wapitis. The first of these, the bison, incorrectly called the buffalo, has the distinction of being the largest animal native to this continent. The males, which are decidedly larger than the females, measure eleven feet in length, six feet in height at the shoulder, and weigh from eighteen hundred pounds to well over two tons. These mammoths of the prairie are so heavy that when a herd of them ran across the plains it made a noise like heavy thunder and vibrations that were mistaken for earthquakes.

The bison is very unusual in appearance and has come to be considered as a typical American animal in the eyes of those who live outside this continent. It has long, matted and shaggy hair, which is especially long on the head, neck, and forelegs; short, curved, hollow horns which grow from bony stumps on the forehead; and a rather high, fleshy hump at the shoulders. The color is dark brown where the hair is longest and a lighter brown on the under and rear parts of the body. The bison formerly roamed the plains from Texas to northern Canada and from the Rockies to the Appalachians. They are grass-eating animals and this was the area where grass grew abundantly. With the coming of the white man, however, they were almost destroyed and are now to be found only in wild animal refuges, in zoos and in a few isolated, inaccessible spots in Canada.

An original inhabitant of the mountains of this country is the mountain sheep, also known as the Rocky Mountain sheep, bighorn sheep, bighorn, and Rocky Mountain bighorn. Because of the skill needed in hunting these beasts, they compare with the African lion in the eyes of big game hunters. Although they weigh from one hundred twenty-five to one hundred seventy-five pounds and are often five feet in length and two and one-half in height, the mountain sheep are extremely agile, active and swift. These characteristics make them very hard to catch or to shoot.

In physical appearance they resemble the domesticated sheep, except that they are larger, heavier and more nimble of foot. Mentally they are far superior to their tame cousins. They are easily recognized by their big horns which curl upward and backward and then down and around the ear until they are almost circular. Their food is the tender grasses and young plants that grow above the tree line in the mountains. Since they roam near the peaks of the mountains where it is very rocky and steep, it is no wonder that they are so hard to hunt. Combined with their nimble feet, which enable them to jump gracefully from rock to rock and from crevice to crevice, is a quick wit which helps them to elude their enemies—cougars, wolves, lynxes, and men.

MOUNTAIN GOATS

People are accustomed to thinking of goats as being cleverer than sheep, so it is a surprise to find the mountain goat is considerably less nimble-witted than the mountain sheep. This is because the mountain goat, which is also called Rocky Mountain goat, American chamois, white goat, and mazame, is not a goat but an antelope, like the European chamois. However, the mountain goat looks so much like the common goat that it will probably continue with that name until the end of time.

Courtesy National Parks of Canada

ROCKY MOUNTAIN GOATS

Courtesy National Parks of Canada

ROCKY MOUNTAIN RAM, BANFF NATIONAL PARK, ALBERTA, CANADA

The mountain goat differs from the ordinary goat in that it is a little larger, somewhat heavier, averaging two hundred pounds, and invariably has a long and heavy coat of white hair. It spends much of its time above the snow line where, because of the color of its hair, it is almost invisible. On the other hand it is quite conspicuous when it is looking for its diet of mosses, lichens, grass, and brush and has dark-colored rocks for a background. It is then that it falls prey to its enemy the cougar.

The mountain goat is also a "native son" of the mountains and shares the mountain climbing championship of the animal world with the mountain sheep. The higher, the steeper, and the more rugged the mountains are, the better this goat seems to like it. It is to this agility that it owes its continuous existence, for had it lived in more accessible spots it would have been exterminated long ago.

PRONGHORNED ANTELOPES

Just as the mountain goat is not a goat but a mountain antelope, the pronghorned antelope is not an antelope but a kind of goat-antelope. It is like a goat in that its horns are hollow, but it is also like a deer because it sheds its horns yearly. The pronghorn resembles the antelope and possesses its grace to such a degree that hunters invariably call it an antelope, although scientists prefer to name it pronghorn. Because it possesses features which are common to the goat, antelope, and deer, it was necessary to classify the pronghorn separately.

The most conspicuous features of the pronghorn are its rump patch and its pronged horns. These last are small, slightly curved, and with a prong that curves out slightly to the front. Like some members of the deer family, it has a circular patch of hair, lighter than that on the rest of its body, on its rump. The peculiar feature is that the pronghorn when frightened "flashes" this patch. That is to say, the hair stands on end, much like the hair on a cat's back, and is so prominent that the patch can be seen from miles away when the rest of the animal's body is invisible. This helps the hunter considerably. The animal's curiosity is also an aid to the hunter. Many hunters, on sighting a dis-

Courtesy U. S. Biological Survey

PAIR OF NEVADA PRONGHORN ANTELOPES A BIT DISTURBED
ABOUT SOMETHING

tant pronghorn, merely lie on their backs and wave their feet in the air. Overcome by curiosity, the pronghorn approaches until it comes within range. Formerly ranging from the Mississippi River to the Pacific Ocean, and from Canada to Mexico, the pronghorn is now present in scattered herds in the plains region from Wyoming and Colorado westward.

DEER AND WAPITI

The two species of deer most common to the northwestern section of North America are the black-tailed and the mule deer. These two are heavier and more stocky than their relative, the white-tailed deer, which inhabits the eastern section of the United States. The western species measure about six feet long, and four feet high at the shoulder. The coloring is slightly different, the black-tailed and the mule deers being a yellowish-brown in the summer and a dark gray in the winter time on the head and the upper sides of the body. At all seasons they are white or light gray on the rump and undersides of the body.

The black-tailed deer not only differs from the white-tailed deer in the above respects and the color of the tail, but also in that it has larger ears and a peculiar bounding gait as it runs. It actually jumps rather than runs, landing on all four feet at the end of each jump. This is much different from the dainty gait of the graceful white-tailed deer, but it is much better adapted to the broken and rocky ground over which the black-tails must run.

Courtesy The Colorado Association

MULE DEER FAWN

The mule deer is also a black-tailed deer, but differs from the latter in that its ears are larger and more mule-like and its tail is

Courtesy J. E. Haynes, St. Paul

DEER FAWN IN YELLOWSTONE PARK
As the young deer grow to maturity, the white dots disappear.

SPLENDID SPECI-
MEN OF MULE
DEER IN YOSE-
MITE NATIONAL
PARK

Courtesy U. S.
Department of the
Interior

merely tipped with black, while that of the black-tail is entirely
of that color.

The wapiti is also known by the following names: elk, American wapiti, American stag, and American elk. The use of the term
"elk" is not appropriate, since the wapiti is not closely allied to
the European elk. It is a very large deer, though it is smaller
than the moose in height, weight, and antler spread. It is about
twice as long as, and a foot higher than, the black-tailed deer, and
weighs from seven hundred pounds up to a half a ton. Its antlers
carry from five to seven points, which is a little greater than the
number carried by the antlers of the smaller species of deer. Its
hair is a chestnut brown on the head and neck and grows to the
length of a mane on those parts of the body. The rest of the body
is covered with a light to darkish gray pelage. There is little change
in coloring from season to season, although the animal is a little
darker in the winter time.

GRIZZLY BEAR
FAMILY NEAR
CANYON LODGE,
YELLOWSTONE
PARK

Courtesy Yellowstone
National Park

BEARS .

The kodiak bear, also called the Alaska brown bear, is the largest flesh-eating animal in America. Between nine and ten feet in height, an average kodiak bear weighs between twelve hundred and sixteen hundred pounds. It has an enormous frame, solid muscles, and powerful limbs. Its massive head is set on high shoulders which are accentuated by a tufted ring of hair standing out from the rest of its shaggy, golden-brown fur. Like all land bears, the soles of its feet are bare and when it walks upright it does so with a heavy, lumbering gait that belies the speed with which it can travel when necessary. Its habitat is Kodiak Island and the adjoining mainland of Alaska.

The three other groups of bears to be found on the continent are the grizzly, or "silvertip" bear, the brown bear, and the polar bear. The latter has been treated elsewhere in this volume. The grizzly, because of its fierce aspect, has the reputation of being a dangerous animal. Generally speaking, timberland and mountain bears are shy. Moreover, they have a sense of fun and will

Courtesy Glacier National Park.   Photo by Hileman

"WHO'S THAT COMING UP THE TRAIL?"
A Black Bear photographed in Glacier National Park.

romp for hours. Only when they are hungry or menaced will they give proof of the powerhouse of brute strength that lies coiled under their great, shaggy coats.

Most bears are omnivorous, eating anything from herbs to a deer. They are especially fond of bark, roots, berries, and garden vegetables. But they have an inordinate appetite for sweets and will debauch gluttonously on a wild beehive regardless of the thousands of bees swarming angrily all about them. In Yellowstone, where they are protected, they often break into cabins to raid their larders.

Most bears mate during June or July. They are capable of mating when they are about two years old. The gestation period range is about thirty weeks and the litter averages three or four cubs. An interesting fact regarding their birth is that, quite often, they are born while the mother is still drowsy from her long, winter sleep of hibernation. In spite of the adult size, bear cubs weigh about two pounds at birth, and are blind and hairless.

THE COUGAR

Although the cougar is the second largest of American cats, running to lengths of seven feet including a long, tufted tail, it has seldom been known to attack a human being. One of them has been said to have killed fifty sheep in one night. Most cougars have developed a penchant for horseflesh and have killed many horses by breaking their necks. The cougar has a powerful body, strong teeth, and muscular, clawed legs which enable it to attack almost any living creature. But, through some strange quirk, it fears man. It will stalk him sometimes for hours, but, if it is caught in the act, it can be "stared down" and made to slink away ignominiously, even from an unarmed man.

The cougar generally sports a light, tawny-brown pelt which shades into a dirty-white on the undersides. Its ears are catlike, large and generously tufted with hair. Its body is long and lithe, and when stalking a bird or a deer in the woods, its movements have a sinuous grace which can be found in few animals. Four or

Courtesy U. S. Biological Survey
YOUNG COUGAR PUTTING UP A BRAVE FRONT
Evidently someone is getting a little too close for his liking.

Black Star Photo
REST AND REFLECTION AFTER A NIGHT OF BLOOD
The courageous and ferocious puma, especially destructive in the cattle country, where experienced men are well paid to kill as many of them as they can. Specimens like the above have been known to kill a score of sheep or a dozen head of cattle in a night.

five species of cougars are to be found on this continent, mostly in the western regions, although they were once spread out over the entire country, where they were variously called the mountain lion, puma, catamount, and panther.

The female cougar, running to about the same size and coloring of the male, exhibits a maternal concern for its young that is almost legendary. She will even attack a grizzly bear if her young are menaced. But, strangely enough, the most dangerous enemy that she must protect them from is the male cougar, for, given the opportunity, he will kill his entire litter of young. It is for this reason that the female must seek out an obscure cave safe from the male's efforts to locate her and her babies.

THE BLACK-FOOTED FERRET

Inhabiting the plains of the western states in the Rocky Mountain district, the black-footed ferret has been seen so rarely by naturalists that they are unable to furnish complete case-histories of this member of the weasel family. It is the largest of the weasel family, measuring eighteen inches in length, with a body that is long and tubular, like a dachshund's, and with a similarly lengthened neck. Its feet are so short that when running the animal's movement is decidedly snake-like. Its fur is of medium length, colored a reddish brown that shades into white at the belly. Its tail, about a third the size of the body, is tipped with black. Unlike the arctic weasel, which it resembles in many respects, it does not change the color of its fur to white in the winter.

Prairie dogs form the ferret's main food supply, and when the unfortunate victim has been eaten, the ferret may immediately take over its burrow and use it for a home. When prairie dogs are not available, the ferret will resort to field mice and other rodents, and even to birds and eggs. Like most members of the weasel family, it is nocturnal in its habits. Moreover, it possesses the usual weasel musk-gland which gives off an offensive odor which is a means of defense when the animal is cornered.

THE YELLOW-BELLIED MARMOT

Various species of marmots are to be found scattered over the entire American continent. Because of their adaptability to any climate, these members of the squirrel family are to be found in the heat of desert plains, in the temperate forests and in the frigid mountain peaks of the Rockies. The yellow-bellied marmot of the southwestern United States differs from the other species in that it possesses a beautiful underfur of a golden hue, while its seven-inch tail is a reddish yellow. It is a little longer than the usual marmot, which averages about twenty-nine inches. The color of the yellow-bellied marmot demonstrates the versatility of nature in providing protective coloring for its charges. The northern marmot's gray fur blends in with the grayish surroundings of its habitat, while the golden hue of the yellow-bellied marmot renders it almost invisible in the yellow sands of the desert.

With the changes in climate comes also a change in the marmot's hibernation habits. The northern species, because of the longer winters, hibernates longer than its southern relatives. Peculiar to all marmots is the shrill whistle which they use not only as a means of communication among one another, but also as a sound of warning when danger approaches as they are sunning themselves on rocks or grubbing food.

SQUIRRELS

Three of the most common squirrels found in this region are the western gray squirrel, Fremont's chickaree, and Douglas' chickaree. Fremont's chickaree (pine squirrel) is a red squirrel found in large numbers in the western parts of the United States and Canada. It is one of the smaller squirrels, but it compensates for this deficiency by the great noise and bustle that it makes. On the approach of man or dog it will saucily sit in its tree and scold for hours.

A close relative is Douglas' chickaree which is found only in the Pacific coast regions of Washington and Oregon, since it

HERE'S OUR OLD
FRIEND, THE
GRAY SQUIRREL

Courtesy American
Museum of Natural
History

seems to have a decided preference for the large spruce trees that
grow there. It is slightly longer than the pine squirrel, which
seldom exceeds eleven inches, and its fur is of a darker red, sometimes almost brown. Like the pine squirrel it is very saucy and

Courtesy American Museum of Natural History

THIS CHAP IS NOT A GOPHER, BUT
A GROUND SQUIRREL

inquisitive. Its curiosity often
leads to its death by its enemies,
the hawks, owls, martens, and
foxes. Although this chickaree
is accused of doing much damage, it actually aids in reforest-
ation of the areas of Douglas
fir. It often neglects to dig up
the nuts that it has buried and
these nuts grow into shoots and
eventually become tall trees.

A distant cousin of the
above two, and quite different
from them, is the western gray
squirrel. It is definitely larger
and the color of its fur is a
pale gray sometimes tipped with
white. It is among the most

handsome members of the squirrel family, is keen of eye and ear, and takes alarm very easily. Unlike its reddish relatives, it is quite cautious, flattens itself against branches so as to appear invisible, does not scold or chatter, and uses the ground as a highway much more than the overland tree routes which are the favorites of the pine squirrels and the chickarees. Because it lives in warmer regions, it does not store up nuts, seeds, berries, and buds as do the other squirrels.

PORCUPINES

This very peculiar animal is one of the largest of the rodents, measuring thirty-six to forty inches in length and weighing from fifteen to forty pounds. It is clumsy, moves slowly, has short limbs, a thick and heavy body, and a short, small head. In color it is slaty or brownish-black to black with yellowish-white spines apparent on the rump and tail. These spines account for its not being shifty or clever like so many of the other rodents.

Courtesy U. S. Biological Survey

THE PORCUPINE—ANIMATED PINCUSHION OF THE WILDERNESS

Courtesy American Museum of Natural History

MOTHER PORCUPINE TEACHING HER YOUNGSTERS HOW TO MAKE A LIVING

In some sections the Porcupine is hunted relentlessly because he does so much damage to standing timber.

These spines are generously scattered throughout its fur and are most numerous on the rump and the tail. They are sharp, stiff, and barbed prongs which the porcupine can raise to an almost erect position when it is attacked. Its method of defense is to lie flat on the ground protecting its uncovered belly, tuck its head under its body, cause its spines to stand on end, and await any animal that is foolish enough to attack. With the exception of the fisher and the weasel, most animals give it a wide range. These two, however, cannily turn the porcupine over on its back and attack its exposed belly. Its food consists of the bark, buds, and small twigs of many trees. It has an inordinate fondness for salt which causes it boldly to invade the camps of men in search of this tasty seasoning.

THE BEAVER, ONE OF THE SMARTEST ENGINEERS IN THE ANIMAL KINGDOM

Courtesy Bureau of Provincial Information, Victoria, British Columbia

THE MOUNTAIN BEAVER

Although this beaver-like animal is called the mountain beaver, it is really not a beaver and occupies a family of its own, the sewellel family, of which it is the sole member. Called by the early Indians the showt'l or sewellel, its habitat is confined to the Cascade and Sierra Nevada Mountains, along the coasts of Washington, Oregon, and northern California. It measures about twelve inches in length, looks something like a prairie dog, has a tuft of hair for a tail, and has medium-sized, coarse hair of a dark-brown color shading lighter in toward the belly. Because it rarely leaves its network of burrowed runways which it occupies in a sort of communal life with other sewellels, this little animal is rarely seen by man. Only when it forages for leaves and ferns and tender shoots does it venture out of its hole. Although it can swim, unlike the beaver, it avoids water as much as possible. Ordinarily, it is a harmless, quiescent creature, but when cornered it will show fight and inflict serious bites with its sharp incisor teeth which are actuated by powerful muscles in the jaw. Like the cony, the sewellel has been observed to nip off green growths, pile them up to be dried by the sun into hay, and then to carry them into its burrow for future use. Because it lives in burrows and feeds in dense vegetation, this little animal is not bothered much by hawks, eagles, or owls; but weasels and similar animals have often been found in their dispossessed burrows.

HARES, RABBITS, AND PIKAS

The pika (cony) is a small tailless animal which bears little outward resemblance to its near relatives, the hares and the rabbits. It is seldom longer than seven inches, has buff to gray fur and looks very much like a young bunny without the long ears and bushy tail. With such size, protective coloring, and padded feet, the pika, which lives in piles of loose rock, has great advantages and has thus been able to survive.

Its most interesting feature is that it makes hay like a good farmer. It cuts leaves, flowers, and stems and heaps them in neat piles to dry in the sun. Several times during the day the pika

Courtesy American Museum of Natural History

WOOD HARE—MOTHER AND FAMILY

THE PIKA, "HAYMAKER OF THE MOUNTAINS"
The little pika cuts his own hay, piles it in very neat piles to
dry and season, then stores it away underground for his winter
food supply.

will move his tiny hay pile so that all the plants will dry evenly. In case of a thunderstorm it hurriedly removes all the hay to the dryness of its tiny cave. Thus, when winter comes it has a good supply of food to last it through the snowy and cold months. In the Rocky Mountains where it lives, the winters are very long and many animals starve—but never the pika.

The snowshoe rabbit is more correctly known as the varying hare or the snowshoe hare. It is a medium-sized hare with large hind feet, large ears, though not as large as those of a jack rabbit, a short tail and fur that is brownish in the summer and snow-white in the winter. It eats bark, twigs, grasses and leaves and is eaten by such enemies as the hawks, owls, weasels, foxes and coyotes. This animal is called the varying hare because of the distinct change which takes place in the color of its coats. Its other name, the snowshoe hare, is given because of its extremely long hind feet which act as snowshoes and carry it over the deep snows out of danger of such animals as the lynx.

The Idaho pygmy rabbit is confined in its range to the sage-brush plains of northeastern California, southeastern Oregon and southern Idaho. It is the smallest of the American rabbits, being hardly a foot long, and resembles the cottontail in form and color except that it has no white spot on its tail. It lives in clumps of sagebrush and its coloration is so perfect that it is very difficult to see it. This pygmy does not bound like other rabbits, but stays close to the ground.

Courtesy Field Museum of Natural History
THE FAMILIAR COTTONTAIL RABBIT

Courtesy National Parks of Canada

THE RACCOON

AMERICAN ANIMALS EAST OF THE ROCKIES

WHITE-TAILED DEER

IN TRAVELING through the eastern section of the United States, we meet a widely divergent range of animals. Perhaps the most beautiful animal to be found in this region is the white-tailed, or Virginia, deer. Its motion is so graceful that it is almost poetic as it streaks and bounds through the brush. Its flashing white tail is a singularly characteristic feature as it literally flies along.

The natural life span of the Virginia deer is from twelve to fifteen years. Formerly, however, it is quite probable that very few ever attained their normal life span, because they were a source of food for the early Atlantic Coast settlers. Even as years passed, the lack of game laws resulted in serious inroads on their ranks. The passage of adequate legislation for their protection has resulted, in the last twenty-five or thirty years, in an increase in their numbers, particularly throughout the East.

The southern branch of the white-tail family has difficulty in living a complete, normal life due to the periodic appearance of a plague known as Black Tongue. This is believed to be a form of virulent tuberculosis, and kills the white-tail in wholesale lots when it manifests itself every six or seven years.

The white-tailed deer is found in many sections of the United States, notably from the New England states, down the Atlantic

Courtesy National Parks of Canada

WHITE-TAILED DEER DRINKING

Coast, and then through the Gulf states to Texas. The fawns of the white-tails found in the latter state are peculiar in that they are covered with a beautifully spotted coat. The white-tail thrives well in captivity, and the fawns are easily tamed.

GRAY WOLF

The gray wolf represents, perhaps, one of the most vicious and treacherous animals that ever roamed American plains; while just about extinct east of the Mississippi River, it is still to be found in the Great Plains. The most savage nature of these wolves is exhibited when they hunt in packs. Huge bull buffaloes were put to quite a task to protect their cows and calves when one or more of the marauders arrived on the scene. Even large moose and reindeer have fallen before their savage fangs. Many were the early farmers who found some of their sheep in the morning with just their throats slashed and their bodies undisturbed. A further incentive toward the destruction of the pest has been bounties that are offered to anyone who kills one or more wolves.

These wolves ordinarily grow to a length of five feet, and a height of about twenty-seven inches. Their normal weight is about eighty pounds, although specimens of around one hundred pounds have been caught.

The female, especially, will display an unusual trait if caught in her den. She will hide her head in a little hole and think that she is safe from harm. Needless to say, this makes her capture an easy matter for a wolf hunter.

FOXES

The gray fox, in its general living and breeding characteristics, is just about as opposite to the red variety as possible. It is also not nearly as hard for hounds to catch as is the red fox. While foxes in general are looked upon with dislike by the farmer, the animals can be of great service if poultry and the like are properly housed at night. The fox will, in that case, seek his food in other

Courtesy Chicago Park District

A COYOTE AT PEACE WITH THE WORLD . . . FOR ONCE

Courtesy American Museum of Natural History

THE RED FOX

forms such as grasshoppers, beetles, crickets, mice, rabbits, squirrels and insects, an obvious benefit to the farmers. Some foxes have been known to ignore poultry to such an extent that a ruffed grouse reared its young within one hundred feet of a fox den, with the tracks of the young birds beating a path in front of the den's entrance. The grays are known to climb trees with remarkable agility, either in escaping hounds or in search of fruits.

Another example of dissimilarity between the gray foxes and the red foxes is their ability to adapt themselves to certain regions. The former take to the woods, and are unable to accustom themselves to the open spaces.

The kit fox is about the smallest of his family, and also lacks some of the characteristic speed and cunning usually associated with the red or gray foxes. Its length is about twenty-five inches, and it normally reaches a weight of four pounds.

The kit fox satisfies its appetite with such delicacies as insects, birds, and mice. It is even recorded that it has been seen pouncing on sleeping prairie-chickens in snow drifts. Often, its hunger has proved fatal, because its unsuspecting character has led it to eat poisoned meat intended for coyotes.

The animal, however, is not altogether lacking in intelligence, as evidenced by its action when trapped in the open with its young. The older animals distract the attention of the pursuer, while the little kit foxes scramble back to their burrow.

EASTERN RACCOON

An animal that is typical of north central America is the raccoon, or "coon." He ranges from Alaska to Costa Rica, with

THE RACCOON
WAITING FOR
NIGHTFALL SO
HE CAN SAFELY
VISIT A FARMER'S
BARNYARD,
HENCOOP, OR
CORNFIELD

Courtesy American
Museum of Natural
History

the most frequent species being the eastern raccoon. He is essentially nocturnal, rarely being seen abroad in the daytime, except occasionally on cloudy days.

Although they nest and rear their young in trees, raccoons descend to the ground in search of food. Their main items of diet include frogs, fish, small animals, fruits, corn, grain, shellfish, insects, and reptiles. They do not dive after fish, even though they are expert swimmers, but they do take delight in playing in shore pools, capturing any fish that may be found in such places.

Early pioneers placed much value on the skin of coons, and exhibited great pride in their coonskin caps. Even today, the collegian and the raccoon coat are definitely associated.

It is comparatively easy to track a coon because he rarely travels a great distance in one night, hence the hounds do not have to search far and wide. When found, he will provide the dogs with a short chase, because he would rather seek safety in a tree than in his speed. Dislodging him is not always easy; it is often necessary to fell the tree, simply because he had climbed beyond the reach of human pursuers, and cannot be shaken from his perch.

One of the most interesting traits of the raccoon is his universal habit of washing meat before he eats it. Even those in cap-

Courtesy U. S. Biological Survey

THE MUSKRAT IN FULL FUR AND READY FOR A HARD WINTER

tivity retain this tendency. No one else can do it for them, and unless they are allowed to perform the ablution personally, they will refuse to eat the meat, or else they will eat it under the most vigorous protest.

The larger-sized raccoons are found in the South, and, naturally, their fur is shorter than that of their northern cousins. While they are not fast animals, they can give a dog all he asks for in the way of a fight. A wily coon can stand up to a dog and make the canine wish he had sought other entertainment.

NEW YORK WEASEL—"DIMINUTIVE DYNAMO"

We find another middle western inhabitant in the New York weasel, so named because it is found in large quantities in the region of that state. Its range, however, extends over considerably more territory, reaching as far west as Illinois.

The little fellow is a veritable bundle of high-tension energy, possessed of extreme curiosity, boldness, and complete confidence in its powers of self-defense, along with incredible speed. Nothing short of a bullet can check its dodging, twisting flight. The height of its courage is found in the female's protection of her young. However, a very convincing example may be found in the frenzy and rage of any trapped weasel.

Aside from being a source of exasperation to farmers, the "diminutive dynamo" rids fields of mice and other rodents that exact damage to orchards, crops, vineyards, etc. The appearance of a weasel in any neighborhood usually results in a swift disappearance of many other animals, some even larger than the weasel itself. Many farmers "cut off their nose to spite their face" when they set about systematically to eradicate all weasels merely because some have destroyed poultry. A more logical procedure would be to concentrate on the poultry-inclined individuals.

In common with other members of his family, the New York weasel emits a very offensive stench when he is pursued or cornered. His extreme agility may be well illustrated by the manner in which he is capable of pursuing birds through trees. The extent of his curiosity is so great that immediately after having entered a hole upon being chased, he pokes his head out far enough to avoid missing anything that is going on. Often the trait proves fatal. Weasels have been caught in neglected traps that contained the stalest of baits, not that they were hungry, but just curious about the bait. They absolutely shun vegetation as an item in their diet, living, for the most part, on small animals, birds, grasshoppers, and any other sort of flesh they are able to get.

AMERICAN MINK

Here we have an animal of central North America that possesses one of the most beautiful and highly prized skins, and at the same time a disposition which exhibits great courage and tenacity. Although their length rarely exceeds twenty-four inches, minks have been known to drag mallard ducks and twelve-pound fish for great distances—even, in one instance, boldly stealing the catch of a fisherman who threw each fish behind him on the shore as he unhooked it! And their courage is not inferior: they have been seen besting the heavier muskrat in a fight to death.

THE AMERICAN
MINK

Courtesy Sears Roebuck
& Co.

The versatility of the mink is further enhanced by its expert swimming and successful pursuit of elusive fish. Also, the characteristic scent of the weasel is highly developed.

SPOTTED SKUNK

An animal to which no one will dispute the right-of-way —such is a description of the skunk. A group of skunks can blithely jog along, secure in the knowledge that they are safe. On the other hand, these animals are easily tamed, and are not the least objectionable, even without a surgical operation.

The skunk is ordinarily found in the more temperate climates where his home is in a deep burrow. He has been unjustly ostracized by the farmer, when actually, as in the case of many other

MOTHER
SKUNK AND
YOUNG

Courtesy American
Museum of Natural
History

animals, he proves a boon to the crops because of his diet, which includes beetles, grasshoppers, insects, and mice. On occasion, the skunk becomes bold enough to tackle gophers and rabbits.

The spotted skunk derives its name, of course, from its markings. These are in contrast to those of the ordinary eastern variety of skunk, which has white stripes running through the length of its black coat, even through its tail.

BADGER

The badger, a member of the weasel family, has been referred to as shy and timid. However, its inability to move with the agility of some of its cousins causes it to be an animal that avoids trouble if possible. The animal is very strong, and if brought to bay displays courage of an equal degree.

Its coloring is generally silvery gray, with a white stripe from the tip of its nose extending along its back. Usually, a mature badger measures twenty-eight inches in length and weighs about fifteen pounds. Its principal food is mice, ground squirrels, prairie dogs, and gophers. Since it cannot catch these creatures

Courtesy Sears Roebuck & Co.

THE AMERICAN BADGER

in chasing them, it resorts to digging them out of their burrows. Its long, mantle-like hair affords protection against the bites of other animals.

The badger is a prolific digger, and even though he changes his own home frequently, he burrows more tunnels than he ever uses, thereby furnishing foxes, snakes, coyotes, and other animals with easily acquired residences.

SQUIRRELS

Perhaps the most common squirrel is the eastern gray variety, particularly familiar to the middle-western region. This little fellow is easily tamed, and has a characteristic trait of constantly twitching his bushy tail, which is almost as long as he is. His favorite spot for a home is an oak or pine tree, and he usually nests about fifty feet from the ground.

If he spent his summer idly and failed to store up food for the winter, he would not starve. His keen sense of smell enables him to detect the presence of nuts beneath snow and leaves. His gathering of nuts in trees is often disputed by the woodpecker which has the idea that nuts still on trees belong to him. Instances have been recorded telling how the little creatures have been fascinated by music, often stopping stock-still to listen, even dropping any food that was being carried, and allowing the forepaws to droop listlessly at the side while they sat bolt upright on their haunches.

The thirteen-striped ground squirrel is found a little more to the west, usually from Ohio to Montana, and Texas to Saskatchewan. Since he does not frequent wooded areas, his peculiar

Courtesy American Museum of Natural History

THE SAUCY AND AUDACIOUS
RED SQUIRREL

FLYING
SQUIRREL IN
FLIGHT
Note the wing-effect
of the membrane
stretching from front
to hind legs.

Courtesy American
Museum of Natural
History

striping affords protective camouflage while he scurries about the open plains. His diet consists chiefly of insects, grasshoppers, cocoons, birds, reptiles, insect eggs, and mice, and even its own relative's meat, along with grain and seeds. The latter two articles account for the disfavor in which he is held, and the farmers praise and protect the hawks which prey on the squirrel. The fact that the thirteen-striped ground squirrel eats crop-destroying insects and animals in some measure redeems his own depredations. He stores up non-perishable food that will supply his meals in the spring after he wakes from his winter-long sleep. This is necessary because of a food scarcity that prevails after the winter season is ended.

The largest and laziest member of the squirrel family is the fox squirrel. He is found from Virginia to Florida, and then along the Gulf Coast to Louisiana. The hawk has a real battle on his hands when he tackles this squirrel, which attains a length of twenty-five inches. He is not as nimble as his smaller, noisier brethren, but is more hardy in the winter weather.

Hunting for food is accomplished for the most part on the ground, but the fox squirrel prefers trees. He readily climbs when danger threatens. He also makes his home in trees, in the hardwoods of the North, and the pines of the South.

The most unique member of the squirrel family is the flying squirrel, which is to be found from northern New York to Florida, and west to the plains country.

A thin, parachute-like membrane stretches from the front to the hind legs of these animals, and enables them to assume a gliding flight, which they start with a shove of their powerful hind legs. They cannot actually fly, but with legs outstretched they can glide at an angle as shallow as 20° from the horizontal. Their momentum enables them to curve upward at the end of their flight so that they may land against the side of a tree. Their aversion to daylight has made it difficult to study them very intensely, and their living habits are almost entirely nocturnal.

Courtesy American Museum of Natural History

ANOTHER OLD FRIEND, THE INQUIRING CHIPMUNK

EASTERN CHIPMUNK

Toward the eastern part of the country we find the little brown eastern chipmunk, about eleven inches long, more than four inches of which is a nervous, constantly t w i t c h i n g, bushy tail. Its characteristic mark is a black stripe from the head along its back almost to the tail.

The chipmunk is provided with capacious cheek pockets which are used to carry food or to carry dirt in his burrowing operations. He never beats a path to his door, but strives to approach it from a different angle each time to avoid tell-tale evidence of his whereabouts. While he remains in his burrow on cold days, he does not hibernate, often being seen on sunny winter days.

His scourges are dogs, boys, wild animals, and birds of prey. The latter account for his never seeking refuge in trees unless there is no other means of escape. The fox, mink, and weasel find him a choice meal, and the latter succeeds in capturing him more often because of being able to enter the chipmunk's burrow. Badgers get to him frequently by enlarging the tunnel. A favorite recreation appears to be an assembly of all chipmunks in the vicinity for a boisterous "community chirp."

WOODCHUCK (MARMOT)

This animal, which belongs to the marmot group, has a legendary story woven around his behavior. His hibernating period is from November to March. Every one is familiar with the story that the ground hog makes a preliminary survey of weather conditions on February 2 and returns to sleep if his shadow is visible. He does not store food, but takes on a supply of fat to last him through the winter.

The woodchuck is very particular in the selection of a burrow site, frequently choosing the top or side of a hill to allow for the drainage of his home. He also builds an observation tunnel which he uses in an attempt to spot his enemies before they spot him. The tunnel is frequently used by other animals, such as foxes, minks, or skunks when they are being chased.

Despite the fact that the woodchuck spends all winter in sleep, he apparently spends most of the summer that way, also. He is seen about in the daytime, but he seldom ventures far from his burrow. His expeditions are usually in search of food or for a sun bath, and as a result his physical dimensions are quite sizable at the end of the summer; but he needs all the fat for his winter sleep. Gardens that contain such vegetables as cabbage, lettuce, cauliflower, and celery are the woodchuck's favorite feeding grounds, much to the exasperation of the owner of the garden.

Courtesy Sears Roebuck & Co.

BEAVER PREPARING MATERIAL FOR HIS DAM

BEAVER

The gnawing animals include in their ranks one which has received a considerable amount of distinction and attention. This animal is the beaver, the industry of which has led to the expression, "busy as a beaver."

The beaver usually grows to about twenty-four inches in length, and weighs about thirty-five pounds. Its most noticeable physical characteristic is its flat, horny-skinned tail, which some say is used as a trowel in dam building; and still others claim the tail is used as a sledge upon which other beavers load materials for the dam. It is also used as a warning signal when one beaver will warn others of danger with a resounding slap of its tail on the surface of the water.

The burrow is usually dug so that one entrance is under water, below the point of ice formation. This is for two purposes; the first is that such an arrangement affords protection against enemies; and the second is that the beavers can roam to and from their food storage under the sheet of ice. Maple, poplar, and birch

Courtesy U. S. Biological Survey

THE HIGHER HE CUTS—THE LESS THERE IS TO CUT
Usually, the larger the tree the higher he cuts, while smaller trees
are often cut close to the ground.

bark are their main items of diet. The bark is stripped from trees and fastened under the water surface near the tunnel entrance, where it may be reached all winter long.

In the building of dams, beavers naturally select trees near the shore of the stream. Eventually, this supply runs out and the little animals are forced to get their materials from farther inland. Bringing this material overland to the dam is exceedingly difficult for them, so they further apply their engineering skill in the digging of canals to float the materials and food to the dam site. Oftentimes, these canals have been found to extend hundreds of feet back of the main stream.

HARES AND RABBITS

Hares and rabbits are readily distinguished by a brief examination of ears, legs, and their homes. Hares possess long legs, long ears, and live in nests or "forms." Rabbits, on the other hand, have short legs, short ears, and live and rear their young in burrows.

The "varying" hares are so named because of their varying coat during the different seasons of the year. They are also called snowshoe hares because of the appearance of the hind feet. They usually grow to a length of eighteen inches and weigh about six pounds. The jack hare, sometimes called jack rabbit, has larger ears and legs than the varying hares.

The rabbit family is well represented by the cottontails. Their ears are shorter than hares's, as are their legs. They are ordinarily found from Canada southward. Their enemies are essentially the same as those of the hare, namely, hawks, owls, weasels, coyotes, and foxes. Their diet consists mainly of vegetation, grass, foliage, and bark. Their favorite type of burrow is one that extends under a tree, making it difficult, if not impossible, for larger animals to dig through the roots.

A female rabbit, in the protection of her young, displays great courage and ingenuity in warding off enemies. She will usually fight any animal smaller than a dog by constantly jumping over it, kicking back at her tormentor with her powerful legs. Very few animals, no matter how courageous, can long stand up under such punishment.

**THE COTTON-
TAIL RABBIT OF
THE MOUNTAINS**

Courtesy American
Museum of Natural
History

A water-loving member of the rabbit family is the swamp rabbit. It is normally seen from Georgia to Texas, and up through Oklahoma to Illinois. As its name indicates, its surroundings are the swamps and river bottoms in these areas. It takes to water for its food supply, and also as a safety measure. It is adept at throwing dogs off its trail by such tactics.

POCKET GOPHERS

Another inhabitant of the Middle West, though more often found in the West, is the pocket gopher. Like the mole, he spends much of his time underground, where he feeds on succulent roots and herbs. His long tunnels are dug with his well developed foreclaws, which also serve as adequate defensive weapons. A successful method of trapping him is to lay a rope noose around the mouth of his burrow, and then quickly jerk the noose tight when the pocket gopher sticks his head out the doorway.

Though gophers are loath to leave their burrows, they occasionally wander into a field, doing much damage to crops. Often on these forays, they are spotted by a hawk, owl, or snake, and become a nice tidbit. Snakes usually do not wait for the little pocket-cheeked animals to sally forth, but go right into a gopher burrow and make short work of what they find.

MOLES

Through the states of the Atlantic and Gulf coasts, we meet a little animal that spends its life in almost total blindness, being able to do little more than to distinguish light from darkness. This apparently unfortunate creature is known as the mole, and its propensities for burrowing may well put human "sand hogs" to shame. It digs incessantly for its food, and it must of necessity be a fast digger to catch worms which are trying to escape it. Some observers have recorded its feats of digging tunnels as long as seventy-five yards in a single night!

The coat of the mole is unique in that its hair is short, thick, and very smooth. The fur feels equally soft when stroked either way. Despite the time it spends underground, a peculiar physical characteristic enables it to keep very clean. The mole has a muscle membrane beneath its coat that enables it to shake vigorously any accumulated dirt. Its digging habits have also gained him a measure of disrepute, since it will go to work on a carefully kept lawn with as much energy as it will in a farmer's field.

The mole is a member of that group of mammals known as insectivores—"insect-eaters." The shrews are the closest relatives of the mole. The appetite of the mole is of tremendous proportions. This is well illustrated by observers who have recorded instances of its eating worms totaling its own weight every twenty-four hours. However, the mole will not eat potatoes, and there have been occasions when specimens have been seen starving to death with the vegetable right at its nose. It is easy to imagine the terror that could be created by this animal if its size were magnified to that of a lion, and its appetite and fierceness were correspondingly increased. The latter trait is very evident when two moles meet and engage in duel, usually resulting in the death of one.

An unusual variety of mole is the star-nosed species, its outstanding characteristic being twenty-two cutaneous processes projecting from its nose. Its habits are not vastly different from the previously described variety, and its habitat is primarily in the East and in the central midwestern region of the country.

THE OPOSSUM

The American opossum is the only member of the marsupial, or pouched family to be found outside of Australia. It gives birth to between six and twelve hairless young which weigh no more than twenty-five grains. The young crawl into the mother's pouch where they take sustenance and grow. This period is for only about three weeks after which the young are able to go out and forage for themselves, returning to the haven of their mother's pouch when they are through.

The American opossum's habitat is mostly the southern United States. Its average size is about that of a cat but its head is long, its five-toed legs are short, and its fur is long, coarse and a dirty gray in color. It climbs by means of its long, naked, prehensile tail and hind feet. Being nocturnal it prowls at night for mice, frogs, birds, eggs, fish, insects, and fruit, in fact, for anything small and edible, for it is omnivorous.

Courtesy U. S. Biological Survey

HERE'S A 'POSSUM REALLY PLAYING 'POSSUM

One of the favorite sports in the South is the 'possum hunt. Many find its flesh delicious and its pelt has found quite a market in fur coats. In these hunts, an especially trained dog trees the animal. This done, the hunters shake the tree until the animal is dislodged from its perch. Because of its curling tail and hind feet, this task is not very easy. Strangely enough, once the opossum is brought to the ground, it curls itself up into a ball and feigns death. Its limbs become motionless, its breathing is almost imperceptible, and from all appearances it appears to be dead in spite of the rough handling given it by the dogs and the men. Some attribute this histrionic ability to an innate cunning of the animal. But there are many who, through experiments, have come to the conclusion that the animal is not "playing 'possum" deliberately but has "fainted" through fear into a sort of cataleptic trance. Whatever the reason may be, the animal renders itself harmless by this act, and although it could be capable of defending itself quite readily with its sharp teeth, it becomes an easy prey for the dogs and a delicious morsel of food for the hunters.

Courtesy Field Museum of Natural History

MOUSE OPOSSUM, A TROPICAL MEMBER OF THE OPOSSUM FAMILY

BIRDS OF NORTH AMERICA

I T WOULD BE IMPOSSIBLE in this short section to name and describe all of the birds of North America. This can very well be understood when it is realized that in North America alone over eight hundred distinct species of wild birds and four hundred subspecies have been recorded. Therefore, in this chapter, the attempt will be made to describe a specially culled few about which something odd and interesting can be told. Since such a choice is more or less arbitrary, it would be impossible to name them in geographical order, therefore, they are presented here with no specific listing.

THE EAGLE

Two kinds of eagles are inhabitants of North America. The bald eagle, so-called because of the white head on the adult bird, can be found scattered over the continent's forest regions. The golden eagle is now restricted to the mountains of the West. Because the two are similar in many respects, it is sometimes difficult to distinguish between them, but a sure way of doing so is to examine the lower legs of the birds. If they are covered with feathers, the bird is a golden eagle; if they are naked of feathers it is a bald eagle.

In size these noble birds run to about three feet with a wing spread of between seven and seven and one-half feet. The golden eagle in particular, which is the American emblem, is a majestic-looking bird, not only when it is still but also when it is soaring in

GOLDEN EAGLES
IN LINCOLN
PARK, CHICAGO

Courtesy Chicago Park
District

flight. Its feathers are dark brown except for its tail which is white touched with gray. The bald eagle feeds almost exclusively on fish and when it cannot steal it from an osprey, it will feed on dead fish stranded on the beach. But the golden eagle is a noble hunter. Its eyes are located on both sides of the head so that each cannot look at an object at the same time. Soaring high in the sky, it can spot its prey on the ground, swoop down with a mighty zoom and pounce on an unwary rabbit or prairie dog. With its cruel, curved claws, three of which point forward while the other juts out in the back, it kills its food. Then, with its sharp, hooked bill, which is like a parrot's, it tears the flesh to pieces.

The golden eagle's eyrie, where it makes its nest, is usually on a high, insurmountable cliff or on the top of a tall sycamore or pine tree. It first builds a five-foot base composed of sturdy branches which it lines with grass, leaves, and twigs. Every year, it returns to the same nest adding to it, until eventually it becomes almost a five-foot cube. In this nest, the female lays two white eggs, spotted, speckled, and blotched with brown and purple.

In some sections of the country, eagles are very useful in ridding the area of harmful rodents which destroy grain and other vegetable matter. But where these rodents are scarce and where rabbits, woodchucks, prairie dogs, turkeys, and grouse are not available, the eagle will prey on sheep, goats, pigs, and poultry and carry off a great number. Sometimes, they have been known to carry off small children and attack a man, but such reports are mostly unauthenticated, although an eagle in Hollywood has been trained to swoop down on a small child and carry it to the limit of the wires which hold the bird.

THE SHRIKE—A BUTCHER

Another flesh-eating bird of this continent is the shrike, of which there are two species, the northern and loggerhead shrike. This bird averages about ten inches in length, is a light grayish-blue on the upper part and white underneath with wings and tail of black. It nests in bushes and particularly in thorny trees, the reason for which will be explained. It lays from four to six pale bluish-green, purple-spotted eggs. In the summer, it breeds in the North, around northwestern Alaska and northern Mackenzie; but in the winter it migrates to California, Arizona, and other parts of the South. One of its other names, the butcher bird, is given with reason. It has the habit of killing insects, small birds, and small mammals, like mice, and impaling them on long, sharp-pointed thorns or in the clefts of branches. This done, it starts in to eat its catch. Oftentimes, it goes about sticking its prey on thorns and forgets completely about eating them. The only reason birdmen can adduce to account for this peculiar trait is that the shrike's claws are too weak to enable it to tear its food apart, as does the hawk, for instance, with its talons. Ordinarily, the shrike's call is a harsh, grating cry, but some of them have been known to warble a song, mainly to trap unwary birds.

Courtesy American Museum of Natural History

IMPERIAL AND DOWNY WOOD-
PECKERS ON THE SAME TREE

Courtesy University of Iowa Museum of Natural History

SCENE ON LAYSAN ISLAND, FAVORITE NESTING GROUND OF THE LAYSAN
ALBATROSS

THE ALBATROSS—AN OBJECT OF SUPERSTITION

"At length did cross an albatross."

It was with these words that Coleridge ushered in the bird that was to be the omen of so much trouble in the "Rime of the Ancient Mariner." This bird, the largest that inhabits North America, with a wing spread of more than twelve feet, has always been the subject of superstition with sailors. Perhaps the main reason for this is that the bird follows ships for miles and miles without appearing to move its wings in flight. Apparently it makes good use of wind currents for, in calm weather, it is often noticed to flap its wings heavily to sustain flight.

Two species of albatross, the black-footed and the laysan, frequent the western shores of the continent, the former the northern coast and the latter the southern coast. Usually, they are about three feet in length, are various shades of brown above and white below with short tails and long wings that, when folded, reach to the end of the tail. They lay but one egg on a little mound either in Laysan Island or some other small island in the Pacific.

The albatross feeds on small fish, jellyfish, cuttlefish, and refuse thrown off by ocean liners; swooping down with a bleating croak into the waters to retrieve whatever it sees floating on the water. Having snapped up the food, it starts to flap its ungainly wings, apparently walks on the water for about two hundred and fifty feet, rises slightly above the surface, retracts its legs and is off into the air again.

THE OYSTER CATCHER

If one has watched a man trying to pry open an oyster with a knife, he will fully realize just how strong are the head muscles

SOOTY-BACKED
TERNS   NESTING
O N   L A Y S A N
      ISLAND

and bill of the oyster catcher, also known as the sea crow. This bird, about twenty-one inches in length, seizes hold of an oyster, a mussel or a clam, inserts its bright red, wedge-shaped bill into the side, pries the shells apart and swallows the delicious morsel inside. However, it is not very easy to watch this bird for any length of time because it is very shy and suspicious of anything that might threaten danger.

Being marine birds, they can be found mostly near ocean shores where they forage for water worms and insects when they cannot get shellfish. They make no nest, laying their two or three eggs in small depressions of the sand. Opinion varies as to the manner of the incubation of the eggs. Some authorities state that the female covers over her eggs with sand and allows the sun to warm them. Others say that she hatches them in the daytime and covers them with sand at night or on cloudy days.

The oyster catcher is quite a colorful bird. Its long bill is usually red, tipped with yellow. The entire head is a deep, glossy black, almost blue-black. Its back feathers are brown while its tail feathers are white shading into brown and black. The underside is almost a pure white. Its long legs are a pale purple in color. Strangely, it possesses only three toes, the hind toe being missing.

MAN O' WAR

These birds have been very aptly named. Large, speedy, and truculent, they attack smaller birds and force them to release their hold on whatever food they may have picked up. They do not even worry if the food is partially swallowed. If such is the case, they force the victim to disgorge its food and then swoop down for it catching it as it falls. The Eskimos often refer to it as the "cannibal" bird and they say that, at one time, the man o' war ate human flesh. Usually, they will hunt in pairs and worry and harass a victim until it is forced to give up its morsel.

In size, the man o' war attains a length of about twenty inches. Its plumage is a brownish black above shading into white below. Two long, pointed middle tail feathers stick out behind. It nests in a hole in the ground which is usually near a body of water and lines the hole with grass and leaves. Its two or three eggs are either

Courtesy University of Iowa Museum of Natural History

MAN O' WAR BIRDS NESTING ON LAYSAN ISLAND

green, olive, brown, or gray and are blotched with brown or lavender. Its habitat is in the extreme northern part of the continent and it has been known to winter from the Aleutian Islands to as far south as Australia and the Cape of Good Hope. Although it is most commonly known as the man o' war, it is also variously called the boatswain, skaitbird, dung hunter, Richardson's jaeger, black-toed gull, arctic hawk gull, teaser, and marlin-spike.

THE BLUE JAY—A BEAUTIFUL RAIDER

One of the most beautiful birds on the continent is the blue jay. Truly, it could be called "a symphony in blue," for, from the proud crest on its cocky little head to the tip of its tail, it displays a variety of blue shades including violet, cobalt, azure blue, iris, and blue-gray, together with black, white and brown. Its nest is a poorly constructed affair composed of bits of string, rags, paper, grass, in fact, anything the little thief can pick up or steal. It lays but one clutch of between three and six spotted or blotched olive-brown eggs a year. It is widely distributed over the entire country. Perhaps its greatest villainy is its habit of raiding a bird's nest, eating not only the eggs but also the defenseless fledglings as well, although its usual diet is acorns and other vegetable matter. Its call can, at times, be a sweet, almost bell-like warble. At other times it can have the guttural harshness of a crow, for the blue jay is a mimic and can imitate not only birds, but the sheep's bleat, the cow's bellow, the pig's grunt, and the horse's neigh. Occasionally, it will imitate the screaming whistle of a hawk in order to frighten other birds. Hunters hate it because it always betrays their presence with a warning cackle. That it is a mischievous rascal few will deny. That it is beautiful, all will affirm.

THE SPRUCE PARTRIDGE

If the blue jay is the clown of the bird kingdom, then the spruce partridge, which really is not a partridge but a grouse, is its champion fool. Although it is a wild bird, it exhibits all of the trust in mankind that domesticated birds do. It will sit perched on a branch and allow itself to be knocked in the head with a stick or snagged with a leather loop. Trustingly, it watches a man approach doing nothing to protect itself, even allowing the hunter to reach over and grab it with his hand. Although the spruce partridge's flesh is not particularly palatable, except during the summer when it feeds on insects and berries instead of tree foliage, it is rapidly diminishing in numbers, especially in the South where it was once plentiful. Somehow, a hunter cannot withstand the temptation of knocking over so foolish a bird.

The male spruce partridge is about seventeen inches long, with black and gray plumage above and black feathers below, interspersed with white, while the female of the species is a trifle shorter with various shades of black and brown feathers above and a dirty white below, with stripes of black. It nests on the ground and lays from eight to fourteen eggs that are reddish brown in color dotted and splotched with a darker brown.

Courtesy National Association of Audubon Societies

A FAMILY GROUP OF PINNATED GROUSE (PRAIRIE CHICKEN)

THE KENTUCKY CARDINAL

It is entirely fitting that the cardinal should frequent the southern United States. For years, the South has been noted as a place of gentlemanly chivalry and aristocracy. The cardinal appears to be chivalry personified. Practically no other bird is so elegant in his bearing and chivalrous in his attitude to the female. While she is still hatching her two to four eggs, he takes charge of the young birds of the previous laying. He aids them in searching for locusts, beetles, and the various other insects which they feed on. He warns them of the approach of a marauding enemy. If he finds a particularly delicious morsel of food, he invites and leads his mate to the feast. If she is preening herself in her nest, he perches on a higher branch and serenades her with a rich, warbling song that goes *cue-cue*, which she answers with a similar call. Its other calls of *pip-pip-pip-pip*, sounded almost endlessly, followed with an attenuated *ee-ee-ee* and ending with a *cheer-cheer-cheer* are incomparable bird music and gladden the hearts of all fortunate enough to hear them.

THE BEAUTIFUL
KENTUCKY CAR-
DINAL

Courtesy American
Museum of Natural
History

In length, the cardinal grows to about eight or nine inches and is covered over with a plumage of brilliant red. The female's coloring is not as brilliant as the male's. Flying through the air, these birds almost appear to be red streaks of lightning. They nest close to the ground in bramble bushes or thickets and use twigs, weeds, bark, and grass in making their loosely-fashioned nests. The eggs are either white or delicate shades of blue and green blotched over with brown or purple.

THE CROSSBILL

Distributed over northern and eastern America is a very interesting bird with a curious, crossed bill, the crossbill, the only one of its kind in America. Generally speaking, the crossbill is about six inches long, the plumage of the male being a dull red while the female's feathers are a dirty olive. Its wings are long and pointed while its tail is short, narrow, and forked at the tip. The crossed bill occurs only in adult birds.

The crossed bill is a very useful structure. In the summer time, the bird eats insects but in the winter it changes its diet to the seeds of various pines, spruces, and firs. As these seeds are found only in cones, the bird must insert its closed bill into the side of the cone. As it opens its bill again with powerful muscles, it tears

THE BUSY AND
BUSTLING CLIFF
SWALLOWS

Courtesy American
Museum of Natural
History

apart the scales leaving bare the seeds. With its shovel-tongue, the crossbill then proceeds to scoop up the seeds.

During its mating season, the crossbill is heard to trill and whistle various bird songs. Ordinarily, though, its only cry is a sort of *peep-peep*, something like a fledgling chick's. It builds its nest in conifer trees about twenty feet from the ground. Outside, the walls are of twigs, roots, and bark, but the inner walls are lined with soft grass, leaves and fir tips cunningly matted together. The three or four eggs it lays are light green, speckled, and spotted with brown and purplish gray.

THE MOCKINGBIRD

In appearance, with the exception of its long tail and wings, the mockingbird is ordinary, its plumage above being a brownish gray while its underparts are white shading into gray. In song, however, the mockingbird is incomparable. Few birds anywhere can produce such an out-pouring of crystal-clear trills, mellifluous warblings and sweet, liquid melodies. Particularly in the mating season is the mockingbird musically vociferous. Then, perched atop a tree, it will work itself up into an ecstasy of song that exhausts its strength so that it falls from its perch and flutters weakly to the ground still warbling.

Ordinarily, the mockingbird builds its nest of twigs and weeds lined with soft moss about five feet from the ground in a clump of bushes or a thicket. In it, the female lays from four to six light, bluish-green eggs, spotted with brown. When the young birds hatch, the parent birds fill the air with sweet music and the neighboring mockingbirds take up the refrain until the whole forest is sonant with indescribably beautiful trills, warbles, and whistles. This tendency is tragic, for it is by the song of the parent birds that the bird trappers become aware of the existence of young birds, which are best suited for caging.

THE WHIP-POOR-WILL

The whip-poor-will's odd name, as anyone who has ever heard its call can testify, comes from the fact that its song sounds exactly like that: *whip-poor-will*. It can go on for hours at a time, during the night, whistling the same notes. Audubon recorded that he listened to one sound 1,085 times in succession, stop, and then continue again for 390 times.

Although its song has been heard almost by all, the bird itself has rarely been seen. Nature has endowed it with a vari-colored plumage of gray, brown, and black, which blends in with the foliage near the ground on which the bird rests and nests. In the daytime, when it sleeps, it is almost impossible to distinguish it from its surroundings. Only when darkness falls does it wake up and begin its incessant warbling.

The whip-poor-will fashions no nest in which to lay its eggs. Instead, it finds a pile of fallen leaves or rotten wood hidden in a thicket or underbrush deep in a forest where it lays its two ecru or pinkish white eggs that are blotched over with brown and light purple. Practically the only way of finding the whip-poor-will is to stumble onto a nest. If the female is flushed off her eggs, she

Courtesy American Museum of Natural History

"WHIP-POOR-WILL—WHIP-POOR-WILL—WHIP-POOR-WILL"
The Whip-Poor-Will has been known to make his strange call hundreds of times before taking a rest.

becomes a little actress and flops awkwardly to the ground a few feet away. Then, with a series of grotesque floppings, wing-flutterings, convulsions and gasps, as though she were crippled, she attempts to distract the attention of the marauder from her eggs. If the ruse is successful, she flips and flutters out of harm's way and then suddenly recovers her "health" and disappears noiselessly into the forest, her wing-fluttering almost inaudible.

THE WATER OUSEL

The water ousel, or American dipper, is the only member of the dipper family to be found in the United States. Because of its peculiar feeding habits, it lives near rushing mountain streams, particularly in the Rocky Mountains and in California. Its insect food is to be found only under water and this bird has developed a means of diving under water to feed. Loving water, it builds its nest of soft, green moss as close to a waterfall as it can get. When possible, it builds it behind the falls. This constant spray of water serves to keep the moss alive. When the nest is not watered sufficiently, the water ousel has been known to immerse itself in water, approach its nest and sprinkle a fine spray on it of its own accord. Even in winter, when available water is frozen, the bird will dig itself into the snow or dive into a hole in the ice and emerge at another hole.

These water immersions are made possible by a downy, closely-knitted plumage which is usually a slate-gray in color shading lighter into the breast. All ousels have almost pure white eyelids that gleam out in contrast against their brownish-gray heads. In size, the water ousel is about eight inches long. The female lays from three to five eggs that are spotlessly white.

THE ROAD RUNNER

The road runner is just what its name implies—a road runner. With its long-billed head down and with its long tail up horizontally, it will run speedily on the ground in preference to flying. Sometimes, it will pit its speed against a passing horse or automobile and account for itself quite well.

Like the kookaburra bird of Australia, the road runner will attack, kill and eat snakes. But, in the main, its diet consists of lizards, some of which are larger than the bird itself. Because of its plumage, which is colored olive with brown streaks, it can perch in a clump of mesquite, sage brush, or cacti without being seen because its protective coloring blends in with surroundings. The road runner has been accused of rifling quail's nests for eggs, but whatever road runners were caught in this act must have been desperately hungry for food because of the scarcity of lizards.

The road runner builds its nest in thorny bushes or sage brush. Because the bird is about twenty to twenty-four inches long, including its tail which is longer than its body, it requires a rather large nest which it builds roughly of sticks and branches lined with snake skin, bark, and feathers. Ordinarily it lays from four to six eggs but, occasionally, the number varies from two to twelve, which are dead white or lightly tinged with yellow.

Courtesy U. S. Biological Survey

TOP: (left) CATBIRD—(right) WREN
BOTTOM: (left) SPARROW—(right) ROBIN

THE HUMMINGBIRD

The hummingbirds, the smallest birds in North America, are to be found only in the Western Hemisphere. Measuring a scant three and one-quarter inches in length, its body is brilliantly plumaged in iridescent shades of metallic green, ruby red, sapphire blue, a flaming orange, and even luxurious velvety black. As this tiny bird whizzes through the air at an amazing speed, all that can be seen is a nimbus of flashing colors. It feeds on insects and nectar. When it stops at a flower to sip of its nectar with its long beak and split, tubular tongue, all that can be distinguished of the whirring wings are what appear to be twin halos. Only a modern high speed camera is able to catch and record the flash of wings. What is more, the wing-beat is so speedy that it gives forth a steady droning hum which accounts for the bird's name. When it is in flight, the sound is like a continuous whistling buzz. The hummingbird's nest is as diminutive as its owner, about the size of a ping-pong ball with the top sliced off, exquisitely fashioned of plant down, delicate lichens, and gossamer spider webs. It lays one or two eggs which are almost pure white in color. When hatched, the young are tiny creatures and are fed regurgitated insects which the mother forces down into their stomachs with its long bill.

Courtesy American Museum of Natural History

COLONY OF AMERICAN FLAMINGOES AND THEIR STRANGE MUD NESTS

DENIZENS OF THE SOUTHWESTERN
UNITED STATES AND NORTHERN MEXICO

IN THE GREAT OPEN SPACES OF MEXICO and the southwestern part of the United States are some of the most fascinating of American animals. The rolling mesas, covered with the gray-violet of the sage, are the home of the lobo, the gila monster, the bobcat, the rattlesnake, and the ranging herds of beautiful wild horses. The plains of Oklahoma, Texas, and Coahuila, dry and sun-soaked, merge into the mesas and buttes of Colorado and New Mexico and Chihuahua—a vast front yard for the frowning peaks of the Rockies.

The animals which dwell in this region must be equipped to live through the cold months of bleak winters, when roaring gales sweep clouds of snow over the mountains and across the desert plains, piling up deep drifts in the valleys and smothering the mesas. They must be able to withstand the baking heat of the hot summer sunshine, which shrivels the plants of the prairie, leaving only the cactus and the brittle sagebrush and the restless tumbleweed.

TO THE WATER HOLES THEY COME

A multitude of wild life dwells on the banks of the Rio Grande, that great quicksand-infested river which flows out of the Colorado mountains and through the canyons of New Mexico into

A PAIR OF
COYOTES

They appear to be
fighting over a piece
of meat on the ground
at the right.

Black Star Photo

the desert lands, forming the boundary between Mexico and the
United States. Most of the animals are very shy; a tourist, rushing
over the traveled roads in the heat of the day, may see prairie dogs
and jack rabbits, but he will see little else. Most of the animals
come out only in the starlit blue brilliance of the cool desert nights.
To the water holes they come, to drink long and lift their heads
and drink again. Along the margins of the watercourses, when
the scorching sun has set, are the humblest of creatures, the tiniest
and the wariest. They drink cautiously, ever looking behind them
for the approach of the larger animals which prey on them. Little
frogs hop out of the water to catch and eat insects, leaping back

into the safety of the stream, scrambling into the mud of the bottom when an enemy appears. Hunting the frogs and other food are mice, rats, gophers, and ground squirrels, the small animals which are so versatile that they are found in the cold northern forests and in the hottest deserts. These creatures breed rapidly and in large numbers; otherwise they would not survive, for they are the prey of larger animals. The scurrying little mice, with their large ears and bright eyes, are eaten by wild cats and weasels, ferrets and coyotes.

One of the most interesting of the smaller animals is the thirteen-striped ground squirrel. Like many other animals, the markings of the ground squirrel's coat are protective. The seven yellow-white stripes and the six tawny-brown dotted lines between them are similar in color to the ground over which the small creature runs. He is a little less than a foot long and lives in complicated burrows into which he darts when danger threatens. The shape of his body, with its tiny ears and short legs, is well adapted for running through the underground maze in which he lives. The little ground squirrel feeds on insects and caterpillars and on the mice which feed on insects and larvae; the little rodent in turn is food for larger animals, in the constant struggle for existence which characterizes nature.

THE RING-TAILED CAT IS NOT A CAT

Other, larger animals make their way to the water holes, striking terror into the hearts of the smaller creatures that preceded them. Among the most interesting of the larger foraging group is the ring-tailed cat, sometimes called the civet cat, although it is related to the raccoon and not a cat at all, and about it is no strong, musky smell. The ring-tailed cat receives its name from its most distinctive feature, a large bushy tail which is marked with black and white rings. The tail is as long as the entire body of the animal, and the body is about the same size as that of an ordinary house cat. The ring-tailed cat feeds on insects, small rodents, and birds. He is another link in the chain of big eating little, a process which not only insures the survival of the big but also prevents over-multiplication of the little animals.

Wandering across the starlit prairie toward the water hole are other, fiercer animals. Slinking through the mesquite, stalking a prairie dog, is a Texas wildcat, one of the larger wildcats. Moving with the characteristic litheness and amazing agility of the rest of the cat tribe, the bobcat, as he is also called, is dark brown sprinkled with black. Crouching in the chaparral, the wildcat sights his prey, and, switching his stubby tail about, creeps toward it on noiseless feet, springing suddenly upon it with a huge leap. The bobcat while hunting emits occasional bloodcurdling yowls, freezing his quarry in terror. There are other cats which, sometimes ranging north into Mexico and Texas, wreak havoc among the smaller animals of the plain; these are the jaguar and the ocelot. Still more formidable, these cats are fearless, and no four-footed thing is safe from their maraudings, which are fortunately rare.

THE SHRILL BUZZ OF THE RATTLESNAKE

But the scourge of the desert country, a dweller in rocky gulches and sage-covered mesa, in sandy waste and on brushy hillsides, is the rattlesnake. This reptile, smaller than many of the animals which fear it, is rarely the cause of human death. But among the wild creatures of the prairie the shrill buzz of ·his rattles is a clarion of danger and woe to the gopher or prairie dog which does not heed it. The rattlesnake is one of the most successfully adapted of the snakes, which are a highly successful group of reptiles. Many types live in the mesas and bleak deserts of Mexico and the Southwest.

Courtesy American Museum of Natural History

CLOSE-UP SHOWING DENTAL DE-
TAIL OF THE DIAMOND-BACKED
RATTLESNAKE

Probably the most interesting of these is the horned rattler of the Gila and Colorado River desert lands. The tough scales of this grotesque reptile are hard and enlarged at a point above his eyes; they look like horns and give the animal an appearance even more frightening than his deadly brothers. The horned rattlesnake is also called the sidewinder because of his sidewise direction in motion.

Most common of all the rattlers of this region is the prairie rattlesnake, a medium-sized snake, whose markings are similar to those of other rattlers but lighter in color. Here again is illustrated the adaptive technique of protective coloration, for with his mottled, tawny, cream-colored skin the prairie rattler is better hidden even when lying in the bright sunshine on open ground than he could be anywhere in the desert if his markings were as bright and distinct as are those of many of his fellows.

The snake's rapidity as he weaves over the ground is a never-tiresome wonder, but it is when he strikes that he displays the lightning speed of which he is capable. Coiled and sounding his warning whirr, the rattler is a fearsome animal. Between two rock piles he has taken his stand, after lazily weaving out from under the rocks. The hapless rat that chose the path between the rock heaps freezes in terror, staring as the rattler bunches his coils together and continues his relentless buzzing. He sees the glittering beady eyes and beneath them the hollows which give the rattlesnakes the name of pit vipers. He sees the darting tongue as the snake coils, spring-like, ready to strike. The mottled body draws itself tighter together and then springs, the dreaded fangs sinking into the flesh of the rat, pouring venom into the victim like a pair of sharp hypodermic needles. The snake then swallows the animal whole, seemingly an impossible feat, since the rat is considerably thicker than the snake. The jaws of the rattler are so constructed, however, that the seemingly impossible is accomplished. The jaw bones may be disjointed, thus providing amazing elasticity. However, many of the stories of snakes' swallowing larger animals are greatly exaggerated.

Rattlesnakes arouse a deep-seated dread in people which has brought about many other superstitious beliefs about them. The distance a snake can strike is very limited, being less than its own length. The poison, which the reptile manufactures in certain glands of the mouth, is virulent enough to kill the small creatures on which it ordinarily feeds, but its effect on man is often not fatal. The men who live in the desert areas wear boots through which and above which the rattlers cannot strike, and among them, familiar as they are with the animals, there is little fear of the rattlesnake. The rattler is viviparous; its young are born alive. Like all snakes, rattlers slough their skins regularly, but with each molting the horny tab at the tip of the tail is kept and added to that of the previous molting. The age of a snake, therefore, can be roughly estimated according to the length of its chain of rattles, although, because of accidental breakage, the rattle is by no means an accurate gauge.

A FURRY SENTINEL OF THE PLAINS

Peering about from his basement doorway, the prairie dog is probably the most familiar of all the dwellers of the plains. A squat, alert rodent, he stands at the mouth of his hole like a furry sentinel among the clumps of sage and mesquite, shouting friendly neighborhood gossip in his shrill bark, ducking into his burrow at the approach of coyote or rattlesnake or man. The stories of the prairie dog, rattlesnake, and owl living at peace together in communal harmony in the same burrow are pure fiction. The industrious prairie dog digs holes for the other two, but the burrowing owl doesn't move in until the little rodent has deserted the hole, and the rattler is an uninvited usurper who drives out either of the others.

Pauls Photos, Chicago

PRAIRIE DOG POSING FOR PICTURE

The prairie dogs are like fat old burghers as they stand in their desert doorways. The prairie dog, which is not a dog at all, being much more closely related to the squirrels, is about a foot long, with short, close-set ears and large bright eyes. The coat of the prairie dog varies, from

THE WILY AND
CUNNING FERRET

Courtesy Chicago Park
District

species to species, from a rich reddish brown to a pale tawny yellow, harmonizing with the adobe clay or sand of his surroundings. When he "freezes" it is hard to tell him from a heap of earth before his doorway. The little creature is a vegetarian, eating roots and grass and other plants. His burrow is surprisingly deep, extending almost straight down for some fifteen feet and then branching out in a horizontal subterranean cellar from which the nests are dug, like little pockets in the tunnel wall. Four or five feet below the surface there is usually a hollowed-out niche in the almost vertical passage, a platform probably used by the curious little animals when they are frightened into their burrow and turn around to bark at the enemy if he cannot get at them.

ENEMIES OF THE PRAIRIE DOG

One of the most feared of the animals which keep the number of prairie dogs in check is the ferret. Half again as large as the little prairie dog, which furnishes the major part of his food, the ferret, like the rattlesnake, the badger, and the coyote, is a dreaded visitor to the villages of the prairie dogs. He is a member of the weasel family, with the characteristic aggressive long neck and ferocious head of the weasels. His tail is about one-third the length of his body, and his coat is thick and reddish-brown in color, with a black strip along his spine. Across his face is a black mask, branding him the robber that he is. He makes no home for himself, but moves into the burrow of a prairie dog he has killed, living among the villagers of the prairie dog colony like a gangster. The little rodents can bark their scorn at coyotes from the safety of their burrows, but the slim, agile ferret can pursue them into their homes, and his depredations wreak havoc among the helpless prairie dogs.

The bridled weasel also lives in the open plains, a cousin of the ferret and like him a masked pillager of ferocious disposition. His diet is more general than that of the ferret; all sorts of small animals and birds are his prey. The coat of the bridled weasel is darker than that of the ferret, a chestnut brown shaded with darker brown and black, and the tip of his tail is black. His face is whitish, but across his eyes is the telltale black mask from which he receives his name. His face is pointed and his sharp teeth are like little stilettos, efficient weapons in his bloodthirsty trade.

FIFTEEN FEET AT A LEAP

Another familiar inhabitant of the land of sagebrush and mesquite and tumbleweed is the jack rabbit, which is not a rabbit but a hare. It is a large hare, more than two feet in length, and its ears are themselves often more than six inches long. Bouncing across the plains, his long legs send the graceful animal ten and fifteen feet at each seemingly effortless leap, and even when being pursued by fleet wolves or dogs the jack rabbit seems to be loafing along at an easy lope. He twists and turns as gracefully as a bird in flight, clearing obstacles seven or eight feet high as though they were anthills. There are several types of jack rabbit in the region of desert plains and bleak mesas; these fall into two major groups, the white-sided and the black-tailed jacks.

Jack rabbits do not burrow under the ground as do the cottontail rabbits, but make their nests in the tangled matting of underbrush. In cultivated areas there is a price on the hare's head, for his depredations in grain fields and vegetable plots are serious. In spite of all the enemies which prey on the animal, not the least of which is man, jack rabbits thrive and multiply in large numbers. Literally thousands of them live in the areas of the southwest. The black-tailed variety is more numerous than the white-sided and is found in the extreme cold of mountains and the blistering heat of the desert. The luxuriant fur coat the jack rabbit wears is tawny yellow-brown in color, with black showing in it. His tail is black on the upper surface, and in running he does not hold it up as a signal flag in the manner of the cottontail, but holds it in the normal position even in flight, so that the black fur is

Courtesy U. S. Biological Survey

JACK RABBIT ON THE ALERT

always in clear view. Whether the black-tailed jack is crouching in "frozen" immobility or bouncing across the flats, his coloration is deceptive, and against a background of mesquite chaparral he is almost invisible.

LOBO RANGING THE MESA

The gray wolves of the Southwest are among the shyest of all the desert animals. Hunted by men for the bounties placed on their heads, the cunning animals have retreated farther and farther from the haunts of human beings; they are rarely seen except by the roaming *vaquero* riding alone through the mesquite. When his horse shies and snorts at no visible danger, when young calves or lambs are found dead on the mesa, when he sees a gray shadow outlined against the rocks or a sharp-eared shape silhouetted against the sky at night, baying at the moon, the *vaquero* knows that lobo, the wolf, is about. Lobo hunts sometimes with his fellows in packs, sometimes with his mate, sometimes alone. He ranges for miles with a tireless loping gait, searching for meat.

American Museum of Natural History

HUNGRY TIMBER WOLVES

His endurance is matched by his courage and cunning, although he has found that when men are about with their death-dealing guns, discretion is the better part of valor. Lobo is a handsome animal with a friendly, dog-like face, alert ears, and a luxuriant coat. The pelts of wolves vary widely in color, from rich brown to pale yellow, all shades harmonizing with the rocky, sandy, or adobe environment in which the animal lives. The wolf is the same size as a large dog, sometimes attaining a height of thirty inches at the shoulder. He is strongly built, and his appetite leads him to prey on a wide variety of animals, from little mice, rabbits, and squirrels to the larger animals such as deer and antelopes.

COYOTES—YAPPERS AT THE MOON

More common than the wolf in the lonely reaches of desert waste is the coyote. In some ways the coyote resembles his larger brother the wolf, but he is more slightly built, smaller, and his muzzle is more pointed. He is found everywhere in the Southwest, being at once more numerous and less wary than his brother the lobo. Through the heat of the day he sleeps or prowls about in the low forest of sage and mesquite chaparral. Here he feels safe, for a man with a gun can pass within a yard of him without seeing him, so perfectly does the camouflage of his light grayish-brown coat blend with the gray of the desert brush. Even if he is seen, he still has little to worry over, since a few steps will take him into the dense brush in which he cannot be seen. When night falls and the cool evening winds blow across the mesa, when the lamps of darkness light the sky and the prairie, the coyote starts his hunt. He visits the water holes in his territory, slinking along like a gray shadow in the brush, creeping upwind so that his sensitive nostrils may bring him tidings of hunting ahead, without himself being given away and his quarry warned by receiving his scent. In keeping with humbler physical proportions, coyotes prey on smaller and less palatable game than the wolf, eating insects, frogs, snakes, birds, mice, and other small rodents. They follow in the rear of sheep and cattle herds, pouncing on

Courtesy U. S. Biological Survey

A COYOTE RESTING AFTER THE CHASE

any stray lamb or calf so foolish as to lag behind, and when coyotes hunt in packs they attack larger animals such as deer and antelopes.

The most familiar sign of the presence of the coyote, however, is his barking. Here the small gray ghost is an artist, singing for the sheer joy of singing. Many people who have never seen a coyote because of the shyness of the animal, have heard his cries in the night. Sometimes alone, standing on some rock outcrop with his head raised, the coyote howls mournfully to the cold moon; at other times coyotes bark in groups, an echoing and re-echoing chorus which fills the prairie with sound. The call is a series of shrill yapping barks, staccato and rising in key to the climaxing howl.

THE POISONOUS GILA MONSTER

In the hottest of burning sandy deserts, a co-dweller with the cactus—the saber-bristling saguaro whose barrel-like trunk sometimes rises sixty feet in the air—is the dread gila monster. This large lizard is one of the largest in all North America, and it is also the only one whose bit is poisonous. The gila monster, whose name is given the Spanish pronunciation "heela," lumbers across the scorching wastes with a clumsy motion, like a relic of the pre-historic ages of the giant saurians. About two feet in length, the gila is covered with a pebbly coat of tough, bright scales; like the saguaro it is equipped to resist the sun and maintain its body moisture inside an impenetrable coat of armor. The skin is a gaudy camouflage, sometimes black and glaring orange, sometimes a creamy pink covered with smoky purple blotches. Like that of all cold-blooded animals, including the rattlesnake, the blood of the gila monster is warm with the sun's heat in the blinding daylight and cold when the atmosphere cools at night. The reptile, unlike his smaller agile cousins, the little two- and three-inch lizards which dart like drops of water over rocks and in and out of crannies, is sluggish in its movements, although when aroused it can attain considerable speed. The gila monster is bulky; his tail is massive and his squat body is supported by stubby legs. His shape is like that of a gigantic newt. His bite is poisonous, although not, apparently, in the same way as that of the rattlesnake. The poison glands are located in the lower jaw, and it is said that when biting an animal, this lizzard must turn over so that the poison can slide down the grooves in his teeth into the body of the prey. The female gila monster lays eggs in the sand, which serves as an incubator, warmed by the sun during the day and retaining some of its heat throughout the night. The gila monster lives in uninhabited and in fact almost uninhabitable sections of the burning desert and cactus-infested mesa. His appearance is dreadful indeed; he looks like a creature of the lost world—roaming the desert, lost in time.

Courtesy New York Zoölogical Society.   Photo by Bridges

GILA MONSTER OF THE SOUTHWEST

Black Star photo by Ylla

THE JAGUAR; ALSO KNOWN AS "EL TIGRE"

THE AMERICAN TROPICS

HAVING observed something of the animal life which exists under the extremely adverse conditions of the desert, we may now journey south to a vast region where by contrast the conditions are perfect for the development of rich plant and animal life.

The first glimpse into this amazing tropical land is obtained after leaving the central plateau and the mountainous region of Mexico and descending toward the Gulf of Mexico. The luxuriance of the vegetation becomes immediately apparent. At once striking and delightful is the almost incredible variety of plants and animals, and particularly insects, of which there are innumerable species, though not usually many of any one kind.

The ideal climatic conditions—heavy rainfall, high humidity, and uniformly mild temperatures—account for this marvelous profusion of flora and fauna.

Throughout southern Mexico, Central America, and northern South America, these conditions prevail, and much of this area is covered with magnificent tropical forest. This forest probably reaches its finest development in Panama and South America. We may note that this is the largest continuous forest of its kind in the world, covering as it does more than half of the continent of South America.

Competition is keen among the trees and plants in this forest. The trees grow very densely, and the struggle to obtain sufficient sunlight is intense. Some trees grow much taller than others and the result is a marked stratification of foliage. This has been described as a forest upon a forest.

Here and there the giant trees may reach a height of over two hundred feet, extending their topmost boughs above the forest. Below these the crowns of a great mass of trees are woven together by the many vines that creep up their trunks from the ground, forming a huge canopy. This canopy makes a vast irregular carpet upon which flowers bloom profusely and over which myriads of birds and insects wing their way.

Below the canopy there are fairly well defined layers of shorter trees. The amount of light reaching these lower strata is negligible. The shrubs and the herbaceous plants form a well defined stratum above the forest ground. Indeed, there is little wonder that during the brightest day inadequate light reaches the floor, and that plants are practically absent here.

From this picture of the forest it becomes obvious that the best place for life in this jungle is in the tree tops. Since grass and herbaceous plants cannot grow on the forest floor, grazing animals do not exist here. This naturally lessens the number of flesh feeders that prey on herbivorous animals.

Since most of the animals of the forest live in the tangled canopy or hide in the branches of the lower trees, and since a majority of them are active only at night, one may be disappointed on his first trip into such a forest. It is for the most part very silent during the day, but as night approaches the wilderness is turned into a bedlam by the innumerable nocturnal insects, the various tree frogs, the flocks and the bands of howling monkeys. Particularly do the monkeys raise a terrific racket through the forest.

A visitor to the jungle can get a much better idea of the animal life by frequenting a more or less open area in the forest. Natural areas of this sort or clearings made by man offer a wonderful opportunity for viewing the brilliantly colored butterflies and beetles, the tropical birds, and the forest animals that visit the clearing frequently.

As previously mentioned, most of the animals inhabiting the jungle are arboreal, as the trees offer the best opportunity for obtaining food and protection. These animals must be well adapted to this type of life; therefore, it is of interest to note briefly some of the modifications of the body that enable them to live in trees.

It is important to note first that these animals are for the most part small, since larger animals would, by their size, be rendered inactive in such an environment.

Nature has developed many devices that enable these animals to climb with greater ease. The development of the prehensile tail is one of the most striking. Animals which are able to grasp branches with their tails have in reality a "fifth hand." Almost everyone has seen monkeys swinging about in cages, using the tail in this fashion. This type of tail is free from hair in functional places, and like the palm of the hand has sensitive ridges to assure good grip. One may be certain that the monkey came from the American tropics if it possesses a prehensile tail, for Old World monkeys never developed this useful organ. In addition to the monkeys, other American forest animals which possess prehensile tails include the opossums, the arboreal anteaters, tree porcupines and other rodents (gnawing animals), and the kinkajou (a member of the raccoon family). In the tropical rain forests of other continents we find still others.

Numerous tree dwelling animals have sucking discs on their feet as aids in climbing. Many frogs and toads possess them, and they are especially well developed on the feet of the geckoes (lizards). Among the mammals, several Brazilian bats, the tree porcupines, tree coney, and several monkeys have foot discs. Sharp claws are well known as aids in climbing and many birds, mammals, and reptiles have them. The sloths, which spend their lives in trees, have powerful hooks on their feet.

Black Star Photo by Vernon Whitman
ONE OF NUMEROUS TREE-CLIMBING LIZARDS FOUND IN THE TROPICS

A considerable number of animals in different parts of the world have developed "parachutes" which enable them to glide from one tree to another. By means of skin stretched between fore and hind limbs, such animals as the flying lemurs of the Malay region, flying marsupials of Australia, and our own flying squirrels are able to glide for some distance. The flying dragon lizards of Malay achieve the same act by having long ribs which support membranes. The highest development in this classification of membranous growth is achieved among the flying bats that in actuality realize reasonably lengthy flights.

THE NEW WORLD MONKEYS

The vast tropical rain forest furnishes the monkeys a magnificent home. The various tropical fruits and the many insects give them an abundance of food throughout the year. The treetops harbor relatively few enemies, and perhaps about the only time that they must exercise great caution is when descending from the trees to obtain water.

Under such conditions it is no wonder that a large number of different kinds of monkeys are present. The primates of tropical America comprise two groups: the marmosets and the new world monkeys. It is worthy of note that great apes such as the gibbon and the orangutan of the Malayan region and chimpanzee and gorilla of equatorial Africa are entirely absent.

The American monkeys differ from those of the old world tropics in a number of ways. In general, they are much smaller. Many of them have prehensile tails, while those of the old world group do not. Their faces appear more human, and their noses have widely separated nostrils. Moreover, American monkeys do not have cheek pouches, and in only one instance, the capuchin monkey, is the thumb opposable.

The American monkeys do not all have prehensile tails; those that do, include the howling monkeys, the spider monkeys, the capuchin monkey, and others. The squirrel monkeys, foxtailed monkeys, and sakis have long, bushy tails not suited for grasping.

THE HOWLING MONKEYS

As darkness falls over the dense jungles from Mexico to South America, a tremendous roaring emanates from the trees as the different bands of howling monkeys begin their nightly foraging for fruit, buds, and leaves. It seems as though each group is trying to outdo the neighboring bands.

Courtesy American Museum of Natural History

HOWLING MONKEYS

The howlers, the largest of the American monkeys, and reputed to be the ugliest, are remarkable for stentorian powers that few animals can equal. They are enabled to increase the power of their howls by a large bony resonating apparatus which they possess. The sounds produced by a single howler have remarkable depth and volume and can be heard for a mile or so. As they travel in groups of from four to thirty-five, the howlers give forth a combined roar which is deafening when a band is near. It is believed that these monkeys make this noise to frighten away their enemies.

THE ACROBATS OF THE JUNGLE

The spider monkeys, so named because of their slender bodies, long limbs, and long tails, are the aerialists of the jungle and may often be seen performing in the treetops like circus acrobats. Frequenting the tallest forest trees in small bands, they move swiftly by astonishing leaps, sprawling out like spiders and catching hold of boughs by their perfectly prehensile tails. Curiously enough, they lack a thumb, but this does not hinder them in any way.

Most of them are black, or nearly so, with the face shaded by projecting hair which is either light or dark. They are mild,

Courtesy New York Zoological Society

THE RED HOWLING MONKEY OF
SOUTH AMERICA

intelligent, and make interesting pets. Their food consists largely of fruit. Their soft and flutelike w h i s t l e contrasts strongly with the roar of the howlers.

Ten species occur between central Brazil and central Mexico.

THE CAPUCHIN AND OTHER MONKEYS

Capuchin monkeys have faces that appear almost human, making them look like little wizened old men. The head is covered with short hair, resembling the cowl of the Capuchin monks, with the face almost hairless. They are about twelve inches in length, not including the tail, which is considerably shorter than the spider monkey's. Their hair is less woolly than the spider monkey's, of a tawny-olive color with a white fringe around the head. Unless they are thirsty, most of their time is spent in the trees. These monkeys are fond of insects and spend most of their time looking for them. They are not averse to robbing birds' nests of both eggs and young. When tamed, they make excellent pets and soon become fast friends with dogs, cats, and other domesticated animals.

The foxtailed monkeys have l a r g e, bushy, non-prehensile tails. They usually live in small groups of ten or twelve in the outskirts of the forest. They have a morose and savage disposition and, like the howlers, utter loud cries before sunrise and after sunset.

Courtesy American Museum of Natural History

SPIDER MONKEY

MARMOSETS

The marmosets differ from the true monkeys in that they have claws on their fingers instead of nails, do not have a prehensile tail, and do not have wisdom teeth. Their thumb is parallel with the fingers and is not opposable. They are considered to be more primitive than the monkeys. The marmoset has a gray, woolly coat and a long, banded tail and resembles a small kinkajou more than it does a monkey. Its actions remind one of those of a squirrel. Parties of marmosets usually band together and go scurrying through the high treetops in search of fruit and insects. While they are easily tamed and make attractive pets, it is quite difficult to provide for them properly in captivity so that they may live a long time. Great care must be exercised in their food preparation and housing facilities, and if the marmoset should become ill, it demands the attention and care given to a sick child.

Black Star photo by J. B. Guss

MARMOSET FROM PANAMA

Courtesy American Museum of Natural History

A TRIO OF MARMOSETS

KINKAJOU

In the dense, thick forests of South America, we find the kinkajou, or "honey bear," with its short, soft, yellow fur. From central Mexico to southern Brazil, its eighteen inches of bundled energy swings through the forest trees and darts into little caves. Its prehensile tail is, of course, a great aid in climbing. Its appearance has often caused it to be classed with lemurs, particularly because of its manner of sitting on its hind quarters, feeding itself with its forepaws. However, it is a close relative of the raccoon.

THE SLOTHS

The excellent adjustment of arboreal animals to their peculiar environment is further illustrated by the strange, ungainly appearing sloths. They are so well adapted to this life that on the ground they are virtually helpless.

The strong fore legs are much larger than the hind legs, and the feet are furnished with long sharp claws, curved into hooks by which the sloths hang beneath the branches, even when they sleep. The strong claws enable them to move with agility even when climbing up and down smooth trunks.

Black Star photo by William Fox

TWO-TOED SLOTH
Showing characteristic manner of clinging to limb.

The sloths are usually nocturnal, and during the day may be seen hanging motionless in the trees. Their habits have been misunderstood, and the term "slothful" has been used to denote an indolent person. However, they are very active at night, feeding on leaves, buds, and young shoots of trees.

The coat of the sloth is coarse and shaggy. In some species the fur has a greenish tinge because of the presence of many minute one-celled plants (green algae). Strangely enough, the hair of the sloth does not grow in the same direction as it does in other animals. Indeed, it grows in such a way as to hang down when the

TWO-TOED SLOTH
IN ITS NORMAL
POSITION

Courtesy New York
Zoological Society

sloth is normally pendent upside down, and thus it acts as a water shed for the animal.

The sloth produces only a single young one at a birth. The young sloth clings to the mother until it acquires size and strength to provide for itself.

There are less than a dozen species of sloths, all residents of tropical America. They may be classified in two groups, the two-toed sloths and the three-toed sloths. They all have three toes on the hind feet but differ in the number on the fore feet.

The sloth belongs to that fascinating group of animals known as the Edentata, the "toothless" mammals. All members of the group are not entirely toothless; the sloth has well-developed molar teeth for crushing leaves, but lacks the cutting incisor teeth.

Although not toothless, the sloth has many structural similarities to the anteaters and armadillos, the other members of the edentate group. The sloths, anteaters, and armadillos are all confined to tropical America and are the only survivors of a very large group of prehistoric forms. Fossil records indicate that the amazing giant sloths and armadillos must have been a startling sight. The monstrous tortoise-like armadillo had an enormous tail armed with rings of large bony spikes.

TAMANDUA, AN ARBOREAL ANTEATER

It is appropriate to discuss the anteaters in connection with arboreal animals since the little anteater, the tamandua, is well adapted for this type of life and lives almost exclusively in trees. Having a prehensile tail, the tamandua is able to climb about with great ease. Its food consists exclusively of termites and ants. In the tropics, the termites (or "white ants" as they are erroneously designated) build large nests in the trees. With its sharp claws the tamandua is able to open these nests and feed on the thousands of termites present. Only two of the toes on its fore feet bear claws, so the tamandua is sometimes called the two-toed anteater.

THE GREAT ANTEATER

Because of its large size and peculiar structure, the giant anteater, which may reach a length of seven feet, is a ground-dwelling species. This is one of the oddest animals in the world. The head is extravagantly long, slender, and nearly cylindrical. The body is thickly covered with a bush of long, shaggy brown hair, mottled with gray on the head. The throat is black, edged with white which continues upwards and backwards over the front

Courtesy American Museum of Natural History

THE GREAT ANTEATER OF SOUTH AMERICA
This animal's long proboscis is a highly specialized structure suited to its unusual purpose.

shoulder in triangular form until it reaches a point over the haunches. The tail is an immense, bushy structure, almost as large as the body of the animal.

The fore feet of the anteater have been transformed into powerful digging instruments by the development of large claws. The middle toe bears an especially long claw which makes an admirable pick for opening the mounds of ants and termites.

As the insects pour from their nests, the long worm-like tongue darts from the elongated snout into their midst. The sticky tongue, which may be twelve inches long, weaves in and out of the nest with astonishing ease and rapidity, sweeping the ants or termites into the mouth. Since the anteater is entirely toothless, the insects are swallowed whole.

In walking, this preposterous beast rests its weight on the outside edges of the fore feet, with the toes turned in, while the hind feet apply the soles to the ground. Perhaps its claws are too long to permit it to walk otherwise.

Ordinarily, the anteater has a mild disposition, but when the occasion arises it can ably defend itself with the powerful forefeet, even to the point of successfully repulsing a jaguar. Few animals are willing to face those enormous claws.

THE BAT

The only mammals in the world that can sustain themselves in true flight are the bats. The fingers in their forelimbs have lengthened so that they can carry the weight of a web of thin skin which covers the fingers and extends down to the hind legs and to the tail. The result is a pair of wings which, when folded, appear to be an umbrella. These wings have developed an acute sense of touch so that bats are able to fly in the dark and avoid objects with considerable facility. Leaflike extensions of skin around the nose and mouth likewise add to their sense of touch, as do the "cat" whiskers on the upper lip and the unusual enlargement of the external ear. The bodies of the smaller bats with their soft fur look like those of mice. The membrane of wing-skin, however, is hairless.

It is convenient to divide the bats into two groups on a basis of the food they eat. The fruit-eating bats are larger and are

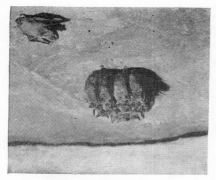

Courtesy Buffalo Museum of Science

A CLUSTER OF LITTLE BROWN
BATS HANGING FROM A CAVE
ROOF

confined to warm regions of the earth. Some of them, the largest bats in the world, may attain a wing spread of five feet. They are in general known as flying foxes. They were formerly said to be bloodsuckers, but this has been shown to be false.

Most of the bats found throughout the world are insect feeders. The true vampire bats, which are members of this group, are found exclusively in tropical America. They are only about three inches long and are members of the leaf-nosed bat group. There have been so many confirmed reports of their bloodsucking propensities that very few question the actuality of such activity. For the most part, they obtain the blood from horses, cattle, and other animals, but occasionally they may suck the blood of human beings. They have sharp-pointed incisor and canine teeth with which to make skin punctures for sucking purposes, and a special pouch of the stomach in which blood may be stored so that they do not have to feed often. In color, they are brown above, shading into yellow below.

The harm that they do is slight. Bats do not deserve the bad reputation that they have obtained, as they are important agents in the destruction of mosquitoes and other noxious insects.

The false vampire is a large species, measuring twenty-eight inches across, with wings spread. It feeds exclusively on insects.

The sucker-footed bat is found not only in Brazil but also in Madagascar. It has attached to the thumb and sole of its foot small suction cups which aid it in clinging to smooth surfaces. The only white bats in the world are to be found in Central and South America. Here, again, nature has intervened to afford one of its charges a protective coloring, as it blends in perfectly with the silvery white sheen of the coconut palm leaves in which it dangles.

Because they are not capable of long flights, bats are unable to migrate as do birds when their food supply is curtailed. This is of importance if the bats live in temperate regions where the winters are cold. Like many other animals, however, the bat is able to hibernate in the winter. Choosing a dark cave or even an attic, it suspends itself by the claws of its hind legs, folds its wings around itself, and falls into a comatose condition that is half sleep and half death. During this sleep there is practically no respiration or blood circulation. This hibernation takes place after the bat has gorged itself fat, so that, during hibernation, it feeds on its stored up energy, which suffices through a period of between three and six months.

THE JAGUAR

We now turn our attention from the tree-dwelling animals to some of those that roam about below. Probably the most impressive of these are the large predatory animals of the cat family—the

Courtesy New York Zoological Society

THE JAGUAR SCENTING PREY

jaguar, ocelot, and puma. These are not strictly terrestrial animals, for they spend a considerable amount of time in the trees in search of prey.

The jaguar, "el tigre" to the natives of Latin America, is a fierce and savage beast. In size and ferocity he is almost a match for the Bengal tiger. In appearance, he resembles the leopard more than he does the tiger, with his tawny, yellow coat covered with large spots which break up into rosettes on the sides.

The range of the jaguar is from Mexico to southern Brazil. Jaguars were formerly found in the United States as far north as Arkansas, but it is doubtful if they occur on this side of the Rio Grande at the present time. Roaming about at all times of the day and night, it is a dangerous foe whether found in the tall grass of the savanna, the trees of the forest, or in the water. Its chief food consists of tapirs, peccaries, agoutis, marsh deer, wild fowl, and large numbers of fresh water turtles. The jaguar swims well and follows the turtle into the water. It has been known to attack a horse in the water, kill it, and drag its carcass to the shore to be eaten. It cannot fare so well with an alligator in similar circumstances, but on land can hold its own even with that fearsome river reptile.

The muscles in its fore-feet and shoulders are solid and knotted so that one powerful blow can break the back of a small animal. Its lithe, lean body is sinuous enough to allow it to climb trees, where it pads silently through the branches for unsuspecting monkeys. There are few instances of a jaguar's having attacked a man, because it fears human beings. But jaguars have been continually hunted because of the depredations they have made upon man's domestic animals. In spite of the fact that it does not prey on man, the eerie cry of one of these animals deep in the dark morasses of the jungle can send quivers of fear down any man's back.

THE OCELOT

Perhaps the most beautifully spotted of all the cats is the ocelot of the South American jungles. The background of its fur is a sort of dark pearl-gray. Its legs are covered with fawn spots edged with black which, as they ascend to the flanks, become eye-like in character. The ocelli, as they are known, extend over the entire length of the body in wavelike chains, in which the eyespots sometimes lengthen and merge into each other. The inside surfaces of the legs, the neck, and the head are colored with spots and dashes. The ears are black except for a white spot at the bottom which gives the ear the appearance of a moth-wing.

Courtesy New York Zoological Society

A YOUNG OCELOT

The result of this variegated spotting is a pelt that is sought after in the manufacture of fur coats.

In size, the ocelot is larger than a cat and smaller than a leopard, running to about four feet in length, including an eighteen-inch tail. In its wild state it is a snarling, spitting, scratching, biting brute that can maul and mangle a small animal to death. It is an arboreal animal and its forages are made in the trees for monkeys and birds. When wounded by a hunter, it will turn on him with a snarl and lunge with vicious swipes of its sharp-clawed paws. Like most cats, however, the ocelot can be tamed and domesticated, providing such steps are taken when the animal is captured young. Even then, there is a possibility that it may revert to type and become an unmanageable beast.

THE PUMA

The puma, or mountain lion, is somewhat smaller than the jaguar and far inferior in courage. Its geographical range is wide: it extends from northern Canada to the straits of Magellan. Unlike the jaguar, the puma ascends mountains which extend ten thousand feet or more above sea-level. It can climb trees with great facility, and having reached a comfortable perch, lies in wait for animals that may happen to pass beneath. As the puma has been described in the section on North American animals, we shall not discuss it further here.

Courtesy New York Zoological Society

THE WHITE LIPPED PECCARY

THE PECCARY

The peccaries are found exclusively in the American tropics and subtropics. They belong to a special family, although they are rather closely allied to the wild boars of the Old World and the domesticated swine.

About the size of a southern razorback hog, the white-lipped peccary is about sixteen inches high. It differs from the ordinary wild pig in that the tusks of the upper jaw point downward rather than upward; the stomach is more complex, and on the hind feet it has three toes instead of four. Its body is covered with stiff bristles, with an extra amount on the shoulders forming a mane, and another fringe under the throat. It frequents the deep forests, traveling great distances for fruits, roots, and grain, and occasionally adding snakes, birds, and eggs to its diet.

The white-lipped peccary often congregates in large herds and does much damage to crops. The farmers find peccaries objectionable enough to make occasional mass kills. The skin of this animal, when tanned, makes a fine, soft glove leather, and many hunters and trappers take regular trips through the jungles to get hides for that purpose. The flesh is fairly palatable, providing the small musk gland of the back is cut off the moment the animal is killed. If this is not done, the oily contents of this gland will drain into the flesh and spoil it for human consumption. Strangely enough, in spite of its fierce nature when wild, if a peccary is caught young, it can be tamed and kept as a household pet. Unlike the prolific domesticated pig which delivers large litters of young, the peccary gives birth to only one or two baby peccaries at a time.

Peccaries are formidable animals to meet in the jungle or elsewhere. Savage, vicious brutes, they roam about in groups, and are totally unafraid of man or beast. They all take the offensive when attacked and can do a great deal of damage with their sharp tusks. Many hunters have been treed for hours by these brutes, and many a hunter's dog has been torn apart by a pack of peccaries.

Another species of this family is the collared peccary, found as far north as Arkansas and as far south as Patagonia, South America. It is smaller than the white-lipped species, and has a coat of blackish-brown bristles mingled with yellowish-brown and white on the sides. It gets its name from a collar of yellow bristles, about two inches wide, which runs around the animal's throat and in front of its shoulders. Where the white-lipped peccary is almost strictly vegetarian, the collared peccary eats practically anything: roots, nuts, worms, insects, birds, reptiles, and even carrion.

THE TAPIR

The tapir might appear to be just another species of pig were it not for its distinctive snout. This similarity is only superficial, however, for the tapirs belong to a separate family which is not closely related to the swine group. The nose is prolonged into a short, flexible proboscis, which is prehensile and used for grasping plants in feeding. Five species of tapirs exist in the world, one in the Malay jungles and the other four in Central and South America. The young tapirs possess a peculiarly yellow striped and spotted coat of hair. As the animal grows, however, the stripes and spots disappear, until its coat is a uniform dark brown. Full-grown, the average tapir attains a length of about seven or eight feet and stands approximately four feet in height.

The tapir's food consists of roots, young shoots of trees, fruits, and berries. Although it is primarily a forest animal, it is quite at home in the water, where it can dive and swim. At first appearance, it may seem clumsy and awkward, but should danger present itself, in the form of a jaguar, for instance, the tapir can move with a speed that belies its bulk. Cornered, it will charge an enemy and effect much damage with its sharp teeth. Its hide is thick enough even to withstand the first murderous slashes of a jaguar's claws, which it can shake off when attacked. It will often enter the water to avoid large predators. A large river such as the Amazon is not always the safest place for it, however, because of the water boas (anacondas) and crocodiles which lie in wait for such an opportunity.

THE LARGEST RODENT IN THE WORLD

South America has one of the most astonishing assemblages of rodents (gnawing animals) in the world. Of the many curious and interesting species we shall mention only a few.

Courtesy New York Zoological Society

THE "WATER HOG"

The largest rodent in the world, the capybara, or "water hog," may reach a length of four feet, and a weight of one hundred pounds. It resembles rather closely the guinea pig to which it is related. Its sparse, bristly hair is a dirty gray, flecked with yellow. It has no tail, very small ears, a cleft upper lip and a blunt, ponderous muzzle. Being an aquatic animal, it has partially webbed toes. Its claws are almost hooflike in appearance. It can dive and swim almost as well as a fish and lives in most of the rivers of South America from the Orinoco to La Plata.

Being gregarious, the capybaras herd together at night, at which time they do their foraging for water plants, bark, and weeds. They often do considerable damage in sugar-cane plantations. The throat of the capybara is unusually small, but, because of its ridged molar teeth, it is able to mash its food sufficiently for it to pass the gullet. Capybaras are easily tamed, but make rather stupid pets.

THE AGOUTI AND THE GUINEA PIG

Another South American rodent, the agouti, is also closely related to the guinea pig. It is rather large, being about the size of a rabbit. Its coarse hair is a reddish-brown. Its legs are quite slender, the front feet having five toes while the hind ones have only three. An active animal, it is usually on the *qui vive* for possible enemies while feeding. It is a nocturnal animal, remaining in its rock cleft, tree stump, or root burrow during the daytime and coming out to feed at night on leaves, nuts, and fruits. When it is near a banana or sugar-cane plantation, it can do much damage, feeding as it does on the roots and tender shoots. Because of its prolific breeding—about twelve young are born each year in two litters—it has been found difficult to control. Unlike most burrowing animals, the agouti sometimes wanders in a herd many miles from its original habitat, taking to the water when necessary, for it is a good swimmer.

The guinea pigs could hardly be more incorrectly designated, since they are not pigs, nor did they come from Guinea. If one wants to find their real home, one must go to Brazil and Peru where the wild cavies live. The guinea pig is a domesticated form of one of the common cavies of those countries.

THE COYPU

The coypu, also a rodent, is most important because its pelt, known to the fur trade as nutria, has taken on commercial significance and is being used more and more in the manufacture of fur coats. Being aquatic, the coypu has hind toes which are semi-webbed to enable it to navigate its fresh-water habitats. Its food is composed of water vegetation, although occasionally, in the evening, it will make a foray on land for food which it snips off with its orange-colored incisor teeth.

THE COATI

Two species of the coati appear in South America, Central America, and Mexico. These members of the raccoon family have long bodies, attenuated, upturned noses, and long tails which are occasionally striped crossways. They inhabit the trees and are very agile. Being nocturnal creatures, they sleep during the day and go out for food at night. In the main, their food consists of birds, their young, and their eggs.

The white-nosed coati, which is more common than the red-nosed variety, has a furred coat of dark brown flecked with black, with a white nose, as its name indicates. This nose, by the way, is hypersensitive to odors, and the animal is able to smell out the

Black Star photo by Alajos Schuszler

SOUTH AMERICAN WHITE NOSED COATI

presence or the approach of its prey even before seeing it. In spite of their nervous and excitable temperaments, coatis can be domesticated into household pets and used to clear houses of rats.

THE ARMADILLO

As pointed out earlier, the armadillos are classed with the sloths and anteaters as edentates, or toothless mammals. Where could one find a stranger trio? They differ greatly in external appearance and habits, yet on the basis of anatomical structure they are fairly closely related.

The armadillo is, perhaps, a typical example of nature's attempts to endow animals with effective means of defense. Covering its back completely, from its neck to the root of its tail, is a casing of invulnerable armor-plate so segmented that, when the occasion of defense demands it, the little animal can roll itself up into a ball perfectly shielded by its natural suit of armor.

The size of the armadillo varies with its species. The great armadillo is the largest and is about three feet in length. Not only its body but its tail is protected with a connected series of bony rings. Second in size is the broad-banded armadillo, attaining lengths of from fifteen to eighteen inches. The five-inch pichiciago is the smallest of the armadillo family.

AN ARMADILLO

Courtesy Chicago Park District

In most armadillos, the armor consists of a number of semi-circular, bony bands, the flesh side of which is buried into the skin, the outside being covered with tough, horny scales. The bands covering the shoulders and the hind quarters are fused together to form pockets for the animal's limbs when they are retracted. The bands of the body, however, are connected by bony semicircular rims in such a way as to make the section flexible and not rigid like the fore and hind parts. Hair growing out of the connecting rims sometimes gives the armadillo a peculiar, furry appearance. This is true, in particular, of the hairy-rumped armadillo. Although it has short, sharp-clawed legs, the armadillo can be quite agile when it is pursued. With its sharp claws it is able to dig itself into a burrow in a remarkably short time.

Ordinarily, most armadillos feed on insects, birds, eggs, roots, worms and snakes. But occasionally they gorge themselves on carrion food, dead horses, and cattle. In spite of this, the South Americans consider roast armadillo a delicacy. Armadillos remain in their burrows in the daytime and can hold themselves so tenaciously in them that they cannot be dislodged. In the night, however, when they go out for food, they can be caught quite readily, provided the hunter is horsed and reaches his prey before it is able to dig itself into a burrow.

THE PICHICIAGO

Most peculiar of all armadillos is the tiny, five-inch pichiciago found in western Argentina. Only the skin along the backbone of this species is attached to the bony shell, which is covered with fine, silky, snowy hairs. Thus there is a space between the body and the inner part of the shell. Its ears are very small in comparison to the ears of other armadillos, since they are merely tiny lobes close to the eyes. Its tail, instead of being long and rat-like, is flat. The hind shield of the pichiciago is a vertical, semicircular disc fixed firmly to the hips. Although positive proof has not been offered, it is said that the purpose of this curious disc is to plug up the hole that the pichiciago has burrowed and thus prevent its capture.

The peba armadillo, found in Argentina, is nine-banded and

lives largely on carrion which it buries for future use when it is sated. Kappler's and the weasel-headed armadillo are other species varying insufficiently to warrant a detailed description.

The natives of South America use the armadillo for a purpose other than that of food. The empty shell is scraped clean of flesh and is bent so as to give it a basket shape, the long tail being fastened to the head as a handle. These armadillo baskets are sold in numbers to tourists as a curiosity.

THE SEA COW

We may close our account of the tropical mammals with a few words concerning the bizarre aquatic forms which live in the Atlantic ocean and large rivers of South America.

The huge manatee or "sea cow" is so different from most mammals that it and its Old World relative, the dugong, are placed in an order by themselves. It is almost unnecessary to say that this animal is not closely related to the cow. Its plump, somewhat cylindrical body is well fitted for an aquatic life. The forelimbs are in the form of flexible flippers, and hind limbs are absent. The rounded tail is broad and compressed and is an excellent propeller. Its face is decidedly unprepossessing with its broad, flat muzzle bearing stiff bristles, its thick lips and small eyes. The head is continuous with the body so that there is no evidence of a neck. The heavy lips are movable and are used to grasp seaweed and other plants upon which these animals feed. The teeth are broad and serve to crush the aquatic plants. Sea cows are rather common in the vicinities of the Amazon and Orinoco rivers and they are able to remain under water for more than five minutes. The largest may attain a weight of nearly a ton. Most of them are about ten feet long and probably weigh around seven hundred pounds. The Florida manatee lives near our own coast but it is nearly extinct.

It is very difficult to keep them in captivity for any length of time. They are gentle, inoffensive animals and appear to have little fear of enemies. They are very sensitive to cold weather so that they are not found in temperate regions.

The Oriental legend of the mermaid is believed to be traced to the female of its close relative, the dugong, which clasps her young with her paddle-shaped flippers while she stands vertically in the water. The female's extreme affection for her young is exhibited by the fact that when the latter is speared, the mother willingly gives up and is easily captured.

RIVER DOLPHIN

A member of the whale group that is met in all oceans and a few rivers, such as the Amazon in South America, is the dolphin. The river dolphins avoid the open ocean and live in large rivers and estuaries. One unusual physical characteristic of the dolphin is its crescent-shaped tail, which is keeled above and below. It possesses narrow, pointed forelimbs, or flippers, and is also provided with a dorsal fin.

No specimen has ever been found of a greater length than ten feet, and ordinarily dolphins do not exceed six or eight feet. But there is a great amount of power packed in those six or eight feet, as attested by their playful antics that have amused countless ocean ship passengers. They usually congregate in schools, and all seem to try to outdo their fellows in leaping, diving, and darting through waves with amazing speed. Their chief food supply consists of fish, crustaceans, and other marine life, but they are also known to feed on their own wounded or sick.

BIRD LIFE OF THE TROPICS

The tropical rain forest shelters an abundant bird population. Many of the common birds of North America have migrated here to avoid the cold northern winters. Falcons hover over the forests of the Amazon. Everywhere are woodpeckers, owls, and martins. Thrushes enliven the borders of the forest with their song. Flycatchers carry destruction among the many insects, and swallows, pigeons, ducks, gulls, petrels, divers, and plovers frequent the clearings and lakes, the banks and the shores.

Thus, many of the birds of the tropics show great similarity to birds found elsewhere; and the same resemblance extends to their mode of life, their manners, and their voices. Notwithstanding this general uniformity and the wide range of many families of birds, the tropic region has at the same time its surrounding world of plants and animals. The warmth and abundant moisture call forth an exuberant vegetation. These favorable conditions likewise produce a multiplicity of animal forms, among which the many birds rival the most gorgeous flowers by the bright color of their plumage.

Tropical America enjoys the exclusive possession of toucans, jacamars, anis, manakins, tanagras, and many other magnificent birds. A complete account of the interesting and unusual tropical birds would fill several volumes. This would not even be possible at the present time, since comparatively little is known of their habits and modes of life because of the inaccessibility of many of the parts of South America.

THE TOUCAN

One of the most unusual and striking birds to be encountered in the tropics is the toucan. It is distinguished from all the other feathered denisons of America by its enormous beak. The body of a toucan is no larger than that of a crow; yet the bill is large enough to give the bird a very awkward appearance. Despite this, the beauty of its color reconciles the eye to its disproportionate size. The bouradi, as one of the three species of Guiana is called by the Indians, has its upper mandible bright red, variegated with black and yellow stripes, and a stripe of sky-blue on the lower mandible. The size of the beak is deceiving, since the horny part is only a fraction of an inch thick, and the inside is filled with a thin network of bone and air. The beak has saw-toothed edges, and is used to pick fruits and capture insects. No reason is known why it should be so large.

The beak of the toucan is a formidable defensive weapon and can be used with great quickness and effect. Any predatory animal must face it when it seeks to force an entrance to the nest.

The plumage of these strange birds rivals the beak in beauty of color, and the feathers are frequently worn by the Brazilian ladies, as well as the Indian tribes which roam through the vast forests of South America.

There is hardly a more quarrelsome and imperious bird than

the Toucan. They are not gregarious but frequently gather in small flocks to feed. At such assemblies, discord never ceases to reign. In rainy weather their clamor is heard at all hours of the day, and in fair weather at morning and at night. The sound which the bouradi makes is like the clear yelping of a puppy dog, and thus the South American Spaniards call him piapoca.

COTINGAS AND BELLBIRDS

Next to the hummingbirds the cotingas display the gayest plumage. As they lead a solitary life in the moist and shadowy forest, they are seldom seen. Some species are cloaked in flaming scarlet, others in purple and blue. They are almost all without song but their adornment amply makes up for the lack of voice.

The campanero or bellbird, a cousin of the cotinga, has a singular and sweet note to his song. He is about the size of a jay. On his forehead rises a feathered spiral tube which is nearly three inches high when inflated. The note of the bellbird is loud and clear, like the sound of a bell, and may be heard at a distance of three miles.

The Brazilians call one species of the bellbird *o ferreiro*, "the smith." Their call sounds as though someone were hammering iron rails with all his might. They are commonly kept in cages and can be heard blocks away. Close at hand they create a terrific din.

MANAKINS AND THE COCK-OF-THE-ROCK

In the deep forests reside the manakins. These pretty little birds range in size from that of a sparrow to that of a wren. The females are greenish, but the plumage of the full-grown males is always black, enlivened by bright colors.

Closely related to the manakins, is the famous orange-colored cock-of-the-rock of Guiana. It owes its name to the comb-like crest it carries on the top of its head. As it dwells in the most secluded parts of the deep forest, it is seldom observed. The Indians prize the beautiful feathers and lie in wait with their dart-shooting blowpipes near places where the birds are known to gather for their courtship ball.

"MOCKING BIRD"

The small black and yellow *Cassicus persicus* is somewhat larger than a starling and has been named the mocking bird, because of his wonderful imitative powers. He is unlike some of the other birds in that he takes up his station near human habitation where he sits for hours, pouring forth a succession of ever varying notes. He has his own song, but he can and does frequently amuse his audience by answering the yelping of the toucans and the cries of the different species of woodpeckers, and even the bleat of a sheep.

PARROTS

The familiar parrot has many points of resemblance to monkeys in habits and tastes. The monkey never sets foot on the ground if it can avoid doing so; but in the trees it springs from branch to branch. This is also true of the parrot in a sense. Its flight is rapid and of short duration. In climbing, the parrot shows uncommon expertness and agility. The monkey possesses a prehensile tail; but the parrot has a large hooked beak. The latter not only uses his beak as a hook in climbing, but may employ it as a crutch when he finds it necessary to walk over uneven ground.

Some parrots are models of connubial love, for once mated, the attachment remains unaltered until death. Members of a pair of love-parrots of Guiana are never seen except in each other's company, each delighting in imitating the other, and when one dies the other soon dies also.

The magnificent macaws

Black Star photo

A TRIO OF MACAWS

have bare cheeks and long tail feathers. Their loud piercing screams are a source of constant annoyance, but their size and splendid plumage render them fit ornaments of palatial gardens. The commanding strength and plumage of the macaw earns him the title of emperor of all the parrots.

THE HOATZIN

For a long time, naturalists were at a loss to classify the South American hoatzin bird. Even now it is placed in an order all its own. In the first place, it is the only bird in which the young have four complete legs. Another amazing fact about the young is that from the time they are hatched they can crawl out of the nest onto a branch. This they can do because they can use their wings as forefeet. The thumb and the forefinger have claws which serve to aid the young birds to cling to the rough bark. Until the bird's wings are full feathered so that it can sustain itself in flight, these claws are not overgrown with quills. However, when the time comes when the quill feathers grow out and cover over the wings, the claws have fallen out and the fingers fused together. After that, the fore leg assumes the shape and form of ordinary birds' wings.

Another odd difference in the hoatzin is that its gizzard has degenerated. The crop performs the functions that the gizzard ordinarily does. Although it is known by a variety of names in South America, the name of "Stinking Pheasant" is most descriptive of the peculiar musk odor that emanates from its flesh when it is killed.

POISONOUS SNAKES

Contrary to popular belief, poisonous snakes are not common in the tropics. As a rule the poisonous ones are slow in movement, live in secluded places on the ground, and are active only at night. Snakes are infrequently seen in the tropics, and one may travel extensively through the forests and not see a single snake. A majority of those observed are harmless so that the danger from snakes has been much overemphasized. No one will deny, how-

THE NOTORIOUSLY DANGEROUS BUSHMASTER OF SOUTH AMERICA

ever, that there are some extremely venomous snakes in the American tropics. The most dreaded of these is the bushmaster, which lives up to its name in its extremely dangerous character. Fortunately it is not common. It inhabits the vast tropical rain forest of South America and is the largest species of poisonous snake in America, reaching a length of twelve feet. The bushmaster is equipped with enormous fangs, and the venom which descends through these hollow teeth is very deadly. In some cases death has occurred within fifteen minutes after a bite. The body of the bushmaster is pale yellow with an irregular design of deep chocolate brown spots. At the end of the tail it has a sharp horny spine which produces a rattling noise as the animal glides through the leaves. During the day it inhabits a hole in the ground and during the night generally lies among the fallen leaves on the forest floor, waiting for small animals to pass. The bushmaster belongs to the family known as vipers, to which the well-known rattlesnake also belongs.

The fer-de-lance is another venomous member of the viper group, and is found in all regions of tropical America. It is closely akin to the northern copperhead and the bushmaster. Possessing a virulent poison, it is one of the most feared of the snakes of this region. It is the most dangerous of the poisonous snakes, since it may at times visit human habitations in search of rats and mice. In appearance it is quite similar to the rattlesnake, though it lacks the rattle of the latter. The fer-de-lance is reddish-brown in color and is recognizable by irregular dark crossbands throughout the length of its body.

The beautifully marked coral snakes are also poisonous. Their name is derived from their brilliant red color bands, which alternate with black bands and narrow yellow bands. There are harmless snakes of similar pattern and coloration and these are much more frequently seen than are the coral snakes, which are burrowing in habit. The natives of tropical America also refer to these harmless snakes as coral snakes. These snakes grasp the prey and chew it in order to inject the poison from their short fangs. Their poison paralyzes the nervous system in a manner similar to that of the cobras to which they are related. They are probably not as dangerous to man as the other because of the small amount of poison that they would be able to inject.

All of the poisonous snakes mentioned above are ground dwellers or burrowers. There are in some tropical regions arboreal snakes which are poisonous. The palm vipers blend so perfectly with the foliage that they are difficult to see among low shrubs upon which they may lie. It is interesting to note that these snakes have prehensile tails, an adaptation to tree life. Their fangs are rather long and their poison is powerful.

Most of the tree snakes are non-poisonous. They are frequently green or bluish in color and difficult to observe when they are at rest.

THE BOAS: NON-POISONOUS CONSTRICTORS

To most people any large serpent is a "boa constrictor." The boas, however, are a group of snakes of the American tropics which kill their prey by constriction. The huge Old World constrictors are pythons. It is also a mistaken idea that all boas are

TWENTY FOOT ANACONDA FROM THE AMAZON COUNTRY

large. They vary in size from the small burrowing boas to the giant anaconda.

The boas are remarkable in that they possess a protruding pair of degenerate hind limbs in the form of sharp spurs. The common boa, which is at home in the trees as well as on the ground, rarely exceeds eleven feet in length. The ground color of this reptile is ruddy brown which becomes deep red toward the tail. Along the back are large saddle-shaped tan spots. This boa, as well as the others, prefers warm-blooded animals as food; either mammals or birds. The common boa becomes quite tame in captivity and loses the viciousness it may appear to have when captured. The tree boa has an elongated body and a long prehensile tail. Its head appears too large for its body.

The giant anaconda or water boa is an enormous serpent which inhabits the large rivers, particularly the Amazon and its tributaries, lakes, and marshy areas. The anaconda is the heaviest snake in the world, although not as long as the largest of the pythons. There is scientific verification for a twenty-five foot anaconda.

The anaconda lies in the water with just its head protruding, waiting for prey. It is greatly feared by the natives although not dangerous to man. Its coloration consists of black crossbars on a greenish yellow background. The females bear their young alive and a litter may consist of as many as thirty young, each of which may be twenty to thirty inches long.

SEA SNAKES

Poisonous sea snakes are to be found in the tropical waters of the Indian and Pacific oceans. In the tropical waters from Lower California to northern South America the yellow-bellied sea snake is at times observed. It may reach a length of twelve feet. It propels itself swiftly through the water by means of its compressed tail. Equipped with lungs which extend far back in the body, the sea snake is capable of remaining under water for a long time. It cannot live for more than a few hours out of water. It subsists primarily on small fish which it kills with its poisonous fangs.

HUGE TORTOISES

Also off the west coast of South America, on the Galapagos Islands, are found huge land tortoises which may attain an age of over a hundred years. The islands received their name because of the presence of the turtles, "galapagos" being the Spanish word for turtles. Since they usually grow to huge sizes, at times weighing five hundred pounds, they are highly prized as a source of food. This factor has practically led to their extermination because they were carried away in great numbers by passing ships. They are now protected by the Ecuadorian government which controls the islands.

The males of the Galapagos turtles are capable of emitting loud roars and bellowings during the breeding season. The food of these huge reptiles consists of leaves and berries. They are very tame in captivity and live for years in zoölogical gardens.

There are several giant marine turtles living in tropical waters of America. Their legs are modified into paddles so that they are at home in the water, and visit the shore only to lay their eggs in the sand.

The green turtle, which often weighs over four hundred pounds, is eagerly sought after because of its edibility. It is either captured when on shore to lay eggs or is harpooned as it feeds on seaweed rather close to shore.

The tortoise-shell turtle, also a marine turtle, is sought for its beautiful horny plates from which tortoise shell articles are made.

CROCODILES AND CAIMANS

These large lizard-like reptiles are well known along the streams and marshes. They are big, bony-armored animals, armed with powerful jaws and tails, and tempers as ugly as their appearance. They are flesh eaters and do not hesitate to attack any animal coming within range of their massive jaws. There are no man-eating crocodiles in South America, nor are there any alligators present.

The American crocodile is quite common along the coasts of northern South America, Central America, Mexico, and the

International News photo

FEMALE ALLIGATOR GUARDING HER EGGS AND NEST

Photo by J. Carver Harris, St. Augustine, Fla.

ALLIGATORS RESTING AFTER A MEAL

West Indies. They are so numerous in bays along the coast of Colombia that people in boats hesitate to go among them. They also occur in southern Florida.

Certain species of crocodilians, known as caimans, are also quite common and inhabit Central and South America. The largest of these is the black caiman of Guiana and Brazil, which may reach a length of twenty feet.

LIZARDS

The lizards are found throughout the world except in the polar regions and on the summits of high mountains. The tropical areas furnish a particularly suitable environment for them, and nowhere else are they found in such multitudes and diversity of form. They occur on all sides; lizards of every size, form, and color, are seen darting, crawling, climbing, and rustling in the forests, on the sands, on soft banks and hard rocks, on trees and on the ground.

The iguanas are the largest and most powerful of the tropical American lizards. Some of them attain a length of six feet. As a rule they have high, compressed bodies which are surmounted by a tall crest of soft, leathery spines. This character may not be very pronounced in the females. The long powerful tail is usually flattened. Their food is chiefly tender leaves and fruits, but small mammals and birds are not refused. Iguanids rest on branches of trees especially over water into which they plunge when disturbed. They swim well. Iguanids are commonly eaten by natives.

The common iguana, inhabiting Mexico, Central and South America in considerable numbers, is primarily a tree-living reptile. It delights in basking lazily in the sun while spread over the outer branches of trees.

The black iguanas of Mexico and Central America are ground-dwellers, living in burrows. They are generally black in color and very surly in temperament, preferring to fight to running away. They are very fleet of foot, easily outrunning a man. When frightened they run on their hind legs in kangaroo fashion.

DAY-SLEEPERS

The geckoes earned their name because of the sound they emit. Sleeping in concealment during the day and scurrying about by night, they usually take up their abode near or in human

Courtesy New York Zoological Society

THIS DANGEROUS LOOKING IGUANA IS QUITE HARMLESS

habitations, where they may be seen darting over the walls and ceilings in pursuit of flies, other insects, and spiders. They have a very wide throat and always swallow their prey whole. They are quite dull of color and very inconspicuous. Accused of tainting every object they touch, the geckoes have been killed in large numbers. On the contrary they are beneficial because of the large number of insects that they destroy.

How the geckoes are able to dart over ceilings in apparent defiance of the laws of gravitation has caused much speculation. Examination of their feet reveals the presence of moderately large suction pads which, with the aid of a fluid secreted by the skin, enable them to stick to very smooth surfaces. In addition, the toes are armed with retractile claws which are sharp and curved, rendering them very serviceable in climbing over rough surfaces.

The geckoes have thick-set bodies, broad flattened heads, stumpy tails, soft smooth skins, and small sucking discs on each toe. These characters distinguish them from all the other lizards. Most of them have lidless eyes with a vertical slit-like pupil.

"CHAMELEONS"

A group of small lizards (Anolis) commonly found in warm regions of America is popularly known as the "chameleons." They are not true chameleons, which occur in North Africa and Asia Minor. They are noted for the changes which rapidly take place with regard to their coloration. This may rapidly change from green to yellow or gray in response to changes in temperature, light, or such emotional states as fright or anger. They are distinguished from the geckoes by their more slender bodies, extremely long, thin tails, and large neck pouches which dilate under the influence of excitement. The chameleons are small and nimble, and very touchy. In spite of their small size, the largest seldom becoming more than eight inches in length, they are very aggressive. When approached they will spring upon their tormentor and try to bite with their small teeth. Indeed, they are in constant warfare among themselves. In escaping from preying animals, or in one of their own battles, they often lose their

Paul's Photos, Chicago

LIZARD WAITING FOR HIS INSECT PREY

tails, but this is not disastrous for within a few weeks another is grown in place of the lost one.

The chameleons also have adhesive pads on their feet which aid them in climbing, but are unlike those of the geckoes. The pads are not at the ends of the toes, but in the center, and are not sucker-like. The large head suggested the appellation of "alligator lizards." The male Anolis is provided with a movable fan-like throat appendage, which when expanded flashes a dazzling hue of red or yellow.

FROGS AND TOADS

Tropical America possesses more different kinds of frogs and toads than any other region of the world. None are more remarkable than the flat bizarre-looking Surinam toad of South America. The female carries her eggs in her back. The skin of the back becomes spongy during breeding season and has many small cup-shaped cavities. After the eggs, which are spread over the back by both parents, settle into these individual chambers, a horny covering develops over each chamber. There the egg develops into a tadpole and then into a tiny toad, which breaks through the lid and emerges.

Equally astounding is a tree frog which appears yellowish at night, due to the secretion of luminous slime by its skin. Its voice is most disagreeable and is said to surpass even the stentorian bellowings of the bullfrog.

The giant toad, which is found in Brazil in large numbers, is the largest of the toad family. It is nearly double the size of the common American toad, often attaining a length of seven or eight inches. When excited it ejects a liquid much feared by the natives, but which is harmless.

Some species of frogs of South America are said to secrete in their skin a poison so deadly that the natives use it to poison their darts. Some of the tree frogs of South and Central America protect their eggs from other animals by depositing them in frothy masses between two leaves overhanging a pond or stream. When the tadpoles hatch they drop into the water and develop into frogs.

Some frogs which lay their eggs in temporary pools move their tadpoles to other places as the pools dry up. The dozen or so tadpoles adhere by suction to the backs of their parents and are carried to new pools.

THE PIRANHA

Of the many fascinating fishes which abound in tropical waters, we have space for the discussion of only one—the notorious piranha. The piranha of the Amazon and other South American rivers, may be only eighteen inches long but, because of its ferocity, it is feared even more than the alligator or the caiman. The piranha's squat head has a lower jaw that can open cavernously. Its teeth are wedge-shaped, like a shark's, and almost razor-sharp. Powerful jaw muscles can close its armored jaw with enough force to cut a man's arm to the bone. Some piranhas have even been known to shear through brass hooks and four-ply brads. The strikingly large and powerful muscular development of the lower jaw has led to their being called "water bulldogs'" by English residents.

If an animal steps quietly into the waters of a river, in most cases, it will remain unharmed. But if it causes an undue disturbance of the water, a school of piranhas may swarm around it, lunge viciously, and tear it to pieces in a short time. They snap one bite out after another with incredible rapidity. Their ferocity is well expressed by their behavior on land as well as in the water. They bite savagely after having been landed, and may produce severe wounds if one is not careful. A native swimmer was once attacked by piranhas. He managed to pull himself out of the water by means of an overhanging branch, but he was a hospital case for six months afterwards. Strangely enough, they are said not to attack a wounded piranha.

The Indians use the piranha's jawbone as a saw. The fish is edible but quite bony. White men cannot enjoy its edibility when they remember that they might be eating a native's arm or leg. Colonel Roosevelt said that the piranha is "the embodiment of evil ferocity."

TROPICAL ANTS

Very few wonders of nature surpass those of the world of the social insects. The student of insects in the tropics may find much to excite his wonder and admiration, but in the end he will find the behavior of the ants, bees, wasps, and termites unsurpassed. We have already briefly touched on the social life of the termites and now turn our attention to some of the marvels of ant life.

One cannot spend long in the tropics without having some experience with ants, often unpleasant because many of the ants of the torrid zone are equipped with stings. If any group of insects holds sway over the forest and savanna, the ants certainly do. The number of species of ants in the world is not so very great, but the number of individuals is inconceivable. The variation in size is from about a millimeter in length to somewhat over an inch. They vary greatly in behavior, some being carnivorous and others feeding exclusively on plant food. A few of the ants hunt alone, many others hunt in great armies. Some of the "vegetarians" cultivate their own gardens, others collect and store grain. A large number of ants build elaborate underground nests, a few utilize the hollow trunks of certain tropical trees, and others that travel in great hordes do not have a permanent nest at all.

The largest ants in the world, the primitive ponerines, carry on their depredations alone in most instances. With large and powerful jaws and a long, poisonous sting, the inch-and-a-quarter Brazilian ponerine ants need little aid in subduing large insects. They are greatly feared by the natives. The pain resulting from their sting is excruciating and may last for a considerable time. These ants are quite frequently observed, but fortunately they are not in colonies and one is not very often likely to be stung by them.

LEGIONARY ANTS

Far more formidable than the savage ponerines are the legions of death which sweep unhampered through the tropical forests of Africa and America. Unfortunate, indeed, is any animal, large or small, which is unable to escape the ravages of an army of driver ants. Marching in columns up to a foot or more in width, these blind ants with their large curved mandibles and terrible stings recognize no enemy too large to attack. Every animal they encounter is dismembered and carried along to be eaten. They climb trees to search in every crevice for insects and other prey; they enter every hole in the ground; and they investigate each log encountered. If one's house is in the line of march, it makes no difference; the horde will pour through it and kill and remove every living thing. At a time like this, retreat is inevitable, for no one can fight such an army. There is one compensation: one finds the house cleaned of roaches and other vermin.

There are few barriers that turn them back. Even a small stream does not deter them, for they will form a bridge of their own bodies from bank to bank, and the army will march on over. The army ants do not have a permanent nest. When on the march, the young are carried in the jaws of some of the workers. The column frequently makes "overnight" nests in suit-

able places such as the hollows of fallen trees, or may construct
a nest of their own bodies, which are placed one above the other
somewhat like bricks in a wall. Tubular entrances, guarded by the
soldiers, lead to chambers housing the queen, the young, and their
attendants.

THE OLDEST AGRICULTURE IN THE WORLD

Wherever one goes in the American tropics, one cannot fail
to be impressed sooner or later by the processions of ants which
are encountered hurrying along narrow, cleared paths carrying
what appear to be green parasols. These are the remarkable leaf-
cutting or parasol ants.

The procession is composed of double columns, and only the
ants going in one direction are carrying sections of leaves. The
others are returning to the scene of the leaf-cutting activities to
scissor out disks with their sharp mandibles.

If one were to follow the ants bearing the leaves, one would
find that the column approaches a mound and disappears into a
hole. It is only by excavation of the mound that the secret of
the leaf-gathering behavior is revealed. Excavation is by no means
an easy task, for the digger would soon be attacked by numerous
soldiers which would rally to the defense of their nest. Considerable blood would be drawn before the nest could be uncovered, as the soldiers have powerful mandibles. Once a soldier
clasps its jaws in place, it will not relinquish its hold even if
the body is severed from the head.

The underground nest consists of an intricate network of
passages and chambers. The chambers contain large masses of
white, spongy material. These chambers are the "mushroom"
gardens and the white material is the fungus itself. Mixed with
the soft white fungus are fragments of fresh green leaves. These
gardens are tended by the smallest workers in the colony, who
are continually engaged in breaking up the fresh leaves into bits
and planting small bits of fungus on them. The tiny "mushrooms" grow readily on these damp leaves and furnish food for
the ants and their worm-like larvae.

The gardens are tended carefully to prevent any other types

of fungi from growing there as "weeds." As the leaves lose their value as material upon which to raise fungus they are removed to the surface of the ground by a second entrance and piled outside. The nest is carefully ventilated so that the proper conditions of humidity and temperature will prevail.

Here, surely, is one of the world's oldest and most efficient agricultures. This subterranean agricultural practice has undoubtedly been going on for untold centuries, probably in much the same form as today. These "mushrooms" are probably the world's oldest cultivated plants. The only comparable situation appears with some African, Indian, and Malayan termites which also cultivate mushroom beds, rivaling these in age and efficiency.

One might wonder how the "seed" for these gardens is obtained when a new colony is established. Careful study has revealed that the young, winged queen before leaving the parent colony to establish a new one, takes a small tuft of fungus in her mouth and stores it in a small pouch until the new nest is ready. Then she lays eggs on the fungus, which is carefully nurtured. As the young hatch they feed on this material until they become mature worker ants, at which time they take over the task of keeping the gardens and collecting leaves.

It is almost needless to say that the planters in many South American countries find little comfort in contemplating the marvels of this ant society, for too many of them have experienced the calamity of finding a group of young trees stripped of their vegetation overnight. These ants do inestimable damage to cultivated plants in these regions, and there is often very little that one can do to control them.

The nests of the leaf-cutters are often very large; in some instances covering a quarter of an acre or more, and probably sheltering more than six hundred thousand ants.

HARVESTING ANTS

In the more arid sections of subtropical America, the harvesting ants may be observed gathering grain. In our own Southwestern states large mounds indicate their presence. There are several types of workers in the colony: the small workers forage about and collect quantities of seeds of grasses and plants and larger workers with enormous heads and mandibles grind the seeds into flour, which is stored.

After the harvest season the large workers are often decapitated, as they are no longer needed and it is easier to rear new ones the next year than to feed them over the winter. Harvesting ants are fierce stingers, and one must exercise great caution in observing them at close range.

ANIMAL LIFE IN THE ANDES

Far above the steaming jungle, in the cloud-topped peaks and crags of the Andes Mountains, from the equator to Cape Horn, is the guanaco, roaming the rugged terrain in wild herds. From this member of the camel family, the Indians developed two very important domesticated animals, the llama and the alpaca. In size, they are much smaller than the camel, do not possess humps and, instead of the camel's splayed, padded feet, have twin sharp-pointed hoofs ideal for mountain climbing. Generally speaking, because of their woolly appearance, they seem to be long-legged, long-necked sheep. In fact, their flesh when roasted tastes like mutton and is sold in butcher shops together with the usual meats. Because of their "water stomachs," they are able to go days without water, like the camel.

Courtesy Chicago Park District

SOUTH AMERICAN GUANACO
The Guanaco is hunted chiefly for its tasty meat.

The guanaco still runs wild over the Andes. Because of the roughness of its short, tangled brown hair, this animal is hunted only for its flesh. The guanaco displays paradoxical reactions at the approach of a hunter. Sometimes, even before the hunter is aware of the guanaco's presence it scents him and is away like lightning. At other times, because of an innate curiosity, the animal will stop when it notices a moving object, and gradually approach it. The native hunters take advantage of this strange trait by falling to the ground and throwing their arms and feet wildly about.

THE ALPACA

The alpaca is one of the two forms derived by domestication from the guanaco. Bred solely for its wool, the alpaca is kept in great herds on the high plateaus of Bolivia, Chile and southern Peru, 15,000 feet above sea level. Its wool is long, fibrous and silky and in various shades of black and brown. Even before the advent of the Spaniards in South America, the Incas were breeding alpacas and shearing them of their wool which they dyed brilliant colors and wove into serapes. At that time and even later, the cloth was coarse; but with the advent of advanced methods, alpaca cloth, as the material woven from the wool is called, is fine and quite expensive, with almost the sheen of silk.

THE LLAMA

Most important of the South American "camels" is the llama, the second of the domesticated guanacos. This animal is only three to four feet in height, but its sturdiness, strength, and vitality are amazing considering its size. Ever since the days of the Incas, the llama has been used as a sort of pack horse. The first record of it was made by Augustín de Zarate in 1544. His apt description should be quoted because it gives a good picture of the animal. Of the llama, which he thought to be an alpaca, he said: "In places where there is no snow the natives want water, and to supply this they fill the skins of sheep with water, and make other living sheep carry them; for, it must be remarked, these sheep of Peru are large enough to serve as beasts of burden. They can carry about 100 pounds or more, and the Spaniards used to ride them, and they would go four or five leagues a day. When they are weary, they lie down on the ground; and as there are no means of making them get up, either by beating or assisting them, the load must of necessity be taken off. When there is

Paul's Photos, Chicago

MOTHER LLAMA AND MONTH-OLD SON

a man on one of them, if the beast be tired and urged to go on, he turns his head around and discharges his saliva, which has an unpleasant odor, into the rider's face. These animals are of great use and profit to their masters, for their wool is very good and fine . . . and the expense of their food is trifling, as a handful of maizes suffices them, and they can go four or five days without water. Their flesh is as good as that of the fat sheep of Castile. There are now public shambles for the sale of their flesh in all parts of Peru, which was not the case when the Spaniards came first."

From this description, it can be seen that in many respects the llama is quite similar to the camel. It has been said that when the Spaniards were mining silver in South America, they used as many as 300,000 llamas for carrying the metal over the mountains to the coast. At present there are about 700,000 of them in South America as compared to 1,500,000 alpacas.

THE VICUNA

In the mountains of Peru, southern Ecuador, and central Bolivia are to be found herds of wild vicuñas, relatives of the guanaco. This animal is smaller than the guanaco, slenderer, more graceful, and with a shorter head. Unlike the guanaco, the rough hair of which is useless for weaving, the vicuña's rust-brown fur is soft, silky and wooly and can be woven into very fine cloth. Its flesh, too, is superior to any of the llama family. However, because of its fleetness of foot and its ability to climb mountain crags, with almost the agility of a chamois, it is very difficult to catch. The natives use the bolas, two heavy balls connected with a leather thong, which they swing around over their heads like a lasso rope and release at a favorable moment. The balls whirl about the animal's legs entangling the thong with them, efficiently tripping the animal. There is still a law in effect which limits the hunter to shearing the vicuña's wool; but because of the flavor of the flesh, the law is commonly disregarded.

SPECTACLED BEAR

A peculiar little member of the widely distributed bear family is the South American spectacled bear, now largely restricted to the Peruvian and Chilean Andes. Its unusual name is derived from the appearance of its eyes, which are encircled by light colored rings. It is the only known species inhabiting the South American continent, just as the African bear of the Atlas Mountains is the sole representative of the family on the Dark Continent. There has been some question as to whether or not the spectacled bear is a subspecies of the black bear, and not a distinct species in itself.

The animal does not grow to the great size of commonly-known bears, its length usually being about three and one-half feet.

CHINCHILLA

Even before the Spaniards came to South America, the people of ancient Peru were using the fur of the chinchilla for ornamental and useful clothing. Because the pelt is made up of soft and lustrous fur, the chinchilla is still a favorite fur for coats and trimmings. Were it not for the fact that these little rodents are so fertile, bringing forth ten and twelve young in two litters every year, their popularity would have made them extinct long ago.

Including its long tufted tail, the average chinchilla measures about fifteen inches in length. It is covered with a coat of soft, gray fur that shades gradually into white underneath. Its ears are long and thin and covered over with fine hair. When it feeds, it sits up on its haunches like a squirrel, with its food, which is usually roots and grass, in its forepaws. It lives in burrows, among loose rocks and shale on the eastern side of the Andes mountains in Chile and Bolivia, where its tightly-knit fur aids it in withstanding the rigors of the cold.

Its burrows are often so deep and inaccessible that trappers are forced to use a sort of weasel to bring the chinchilla to the surface.

THE CONDOR

Among the lofty Cordilleras the condor, the king of all the vultures, makes its home. This royal bird soaring aloft appears as a speck in the sky from the plains below, but in reality it is a great deal larger than a turkey. Its body is about four feet long and its wing-spread approximates ten feet. It is considered an enemy of farmers because it carries off a large number of young lambs and calves. It does not attack alpacas or human beings.

Courtesy New York Zoological Society

SOUTH AMERICAN CONDOR

THE RHEA

Descending from the lofty Andes onto the rolling savannas and grasslands south of the tropical rain forest, we enter the home of the rhea, a relative of the ostrich. It is not so large as the ostrich, very rarely achieving a height of more than four feet, nor are its feathers of the same rich and precious kind. Its feeble wings act as oars to accelerate its zigzag flight which soon tires even the best of pursuing horses.

The rhea differs in other ways from the ostrich in having, three toes instead of two, and in having feathers on its head and neck. It lacks white plumes on the wings and is without a tail.

The male stays at home and sits on the eggs or watches the young. He may sit on fifty or more eggs belonging to several females which lay eggs in the same depression in the ground.

WAISTCOATED BIRDS: THE PENGUINS

Loudly through an antarctic blizzard sounds a hoarse braying cry: the call of the jackass penguin. This "donkey" of the South Pole is a courteous, friendly sea bird, like his relatives which live in vast rookeries below the antarctic circle: emperor penguins, king penguins, cape penguins, and rock hopper penguins. Explorers who have visited the almost inaccessible habitats of the antarctic penguins report that the birds waddle-walk fearlessly toward man, and make an astonishing bowing motion.

Slightly less friendly are the two species of penguins that live in more populous lands. They are the little blue penguins of South Australia and New Zealand, birds about eighteen inches high with starch-white breast plumage and azure back and head feathers, and the Galapagos penguins of the Galapagos Islands, just under the equator. The Ecuadorian government now gives this species complete protection. All penguins except the blue species have glossy white scale-like breast feathers, and blackish-gray backs.

Like the extinct great auk, the penguins have no flight feathers and cannot fly. They are strong, clever swimmers and "row" themselves over the water with their paddle-like flippers. On land they sometimes crawl in four-legged fashion on their wings and webbed feet, but usually they stand upright and shuffle along. By diving and leaping they catch the only food they eat: fish. Penguins in zoos must be fed by hand. They are given fish which they swallow whole.

Nowhere in the bleak antarctic is there a warmed spot where a penguin can place its one egg to be hatched, nor is there any unfrozen nest material. But the penguin solves this polar problem by putting the egg on its webbed feet and crouching down so that its dense feathers cover it. Newly hatched chicks are sheltered on their mother's feet for some time. Due to the severe climate, penguin chicks are always scarce in the flocks. Explorers have seen ten grown birds helping to feed one chick.

The largest species, the emperor, is more than three feet high and weighs up to eighty pounds. Its habitat is the coldest part of Antarctica and it cannot live in warm climates. The emperors the Byrd expedition brought from Little America died in temperate zone zoos. King penguins are only slightly smaller than the emperors.

Courtesy American Museum of Natural History

EMPEROR PENGUINS OF ANTARC-
TICA BROUGHT TO AMERICA BY
ADMIRAL RICHARD E. BYRD

WHAT GREATER SERVICE COULD A DOG PERFORM THAN THAT OF
LEADING SIGHTLESS CITIZENS?

Note how the well-trained Seeing Eye graduate is trying to pull his master away from
possible collision with obstacles besetting his path.

DOMESTIC ANIMALS AND PETS

ONE GROUP of animals we have so far ignored altogether. More important and more valuable to man than all others combined, these animals are also the most common and most widely diffused. Classed as domestic animals, they are found in cities and on farms all over the world.

Of all the members of the animal kingdom only a few have been domesticated by man and used by him as servants or as friends. These live with man on farms and in cities. In their new environment, usually far different from the danger-filled jungles, the sandy deserts, or the leafy trees—the homes of their wild ancestors—these mammals and birds have adapted their nature and habits to their new surroundings. They have grown accustomed to man. They are willing to serve him. They have learned to enjoy his companionship. Many are the stories everyone of us can recall of the devotion of a dog to his master, or of a horse to the one he recognizes as his own rider.

Not all their inheritance has been forgotten, however. Their cries are those of their species. The barking of the dog, the mewing of the cat, the warbling of the canary which can be heard in the twentieth-century city; or the neighing of the horse, the mooing of the cow, the cackling of poultry which break the stillness of the countryside, are the same noises which were heard by ancient man or his predecessor. In times of danger, or in moments of excitement, the "tamed" bull may gore his master as his ancestor perhaps did when he met ancient man in the forests. The claws of the cat, the long canine teeth of the dog, and the hoofs of a horse are reminders of the constant struggle for survival by the ancestors of these animals.

KEEN SENSES

Our pets' sharp senses of seeing, hearing, and smelling seem miraculous because we compare our senses with them. But, in fact, the senses of these animals have actually become less keen. Protected animals no longer need to listen for their enemies and unused or half-used abilities always become weakened. Yet, pets hear many sounds where listening man notes only silence.

Animal sight, except in the case of monkeys and apes, differs from that of man in its lack of stereoscopic vision; i.e., animals do not have true three-dimensional perspective. Moreover, many animals are near-sighted, and most of them appear to be color-blind.

Man early learned that of the wild animals which roamed the woods and plains with him, not all must be regarded as enemies. Some might be trained to serve him. Others might be taught to be companions. Through the centuries man has learned to make

Courtesy Mrs. H. Young, Cedarhurst, N. Y.

CHAMPION BOXER: SIGURD VON DOM OF BARMERE

William Brown Photos, Forest Hills, N. Y.

IRISH WOLFHOUND: ONE OF THE GIANTS OF THE CANINE WORLD

these servants and pets more useful and more enjoyable by selection and by breeding. Thus today's animals of farm and city have been carefully developed.

MAN'S BEST FRIEND, THE DOG

Almost the earliest human beings of whom we have any record seem to have been accompanied by dogs, which were apparently among the first animals domesticated. Certainly the dog has lived with man for ages longer than the horse or cow. Partly domesticated dogs lived with Swiss Lake dwellers. Pictures seem to indicate that man of the Tigris and Euphrates, as well as of ancient Egypt, enjoyed the companionship of dogs. As man migrated over the earth, the dog went with him.

Today a census of the dogs of the earth would be an almost impossible task; they are everywhere. It is estimated there are about sixteen million of them in the United States alone. Seven thousand fifty were registered by the American Kennel Club early in 1936, which was an increase of nearly two thousand in one year. In two decades this list of pure-breds has shown an increase of six hundred per cent. Cocker spaniels, Boston terriers, scotties, and wire-haired terriers seem to be the favorites of dog fanciers.

In Majorca is found an unusual dog. He looks like an unfinished type of greyhound. Refusing to breed with any other kind of dog, this dog has been the same in appearance for at least five thousand years. He looks surprisingly like the crudely-drawn dogs on ancient Egyptian frescoes; and his face is that of Anubis, the Egyptian tomb god. Perhaps the drawings of dogs on the Egyptian bas-reliefs look so crude not so much because they represent primitive art, as because the animals of that long-ago day were themselves crude—only a rough approximation of our sleek modern breeds.

The close relation of the dog to the wild jackal can be seen in the Majorca dog. Other breeds of dogs show a close resemblance to the wolf and from these two wild animals all dogs are descended. The magnificent and diversified modern breeds were developed by man through centuries.

THE GREYHOUND

The greyhound has long been the companion of aristocrats—the dog of kings. For some centuries it was restricted to the guardianship of the nobility by law. The greyhound is believed to be the oldest pure-bred dog in the world, although some scientists credit the mastiff with being the oldest. A dog closely resembling the mastiff is shown on an Assyrian bas-relief dated about three thousand years ago—but the greyhound's supporters point to even older representations. Carvings on the Tomb of Amten, in the Valley of the Nile, believed by Egyptologists to have existed since 4000 B.C., show dogs of unmistakable greyhound type.

In literature, the greyhound was first described by Ovid about the year 1 A.D. Having a gentle, affectionate nature, this is also one of the wisest of the dog breeds. Of course, it is best known for its speed, grace, and beauty.

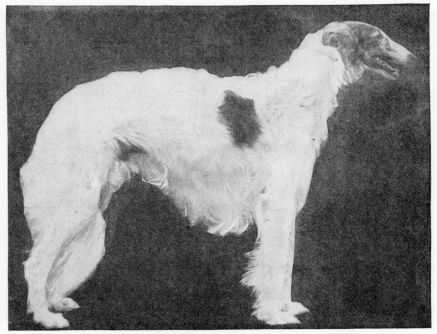

THE RUSSIAN WOLFHOUND
In his native habitat he is something more than a pet. Being fleet of foot,
he is a fine hunting dog on the plains.

This fleet dog hunts the stag, the deer, as well as many kinds of small game, but his natural quarry is the hare—and coursing is his sport. It was for the greyhound that the famous Waterloo Cup Meet was organized in England. When the first meets were held about 1836, they had to be kept "secret" in England, and noblemen paid fabulous sums in order to see the dogs run.

HUNTING DOGS

There are two types of hunting dogs: those that possess keen scenting powers and those that depend more on eyesight and speed. The greyhound represents the latter type, as do the long-eared gazelle hounds of Asia and North Africa. This class of dogs is usually long-headed, small-eared, long-legged, and swift-running. They locate their quarry by sight and overtake it by their marvelous fleetness.

Paul's Photos, Chicago

ENGLISH BLOODHOUNDS IN ACTION

The group which uses its nose rather than its eyes and its feet in hunting is represented by the bloodhounds, fox hounds, and setters. Usually they are thick-skulled, flap-eared. These dogs have been taught to track down their quarry.

Wherever men or animals walk they leave a trail. It may be a visible trail of footprints or hoof marks; this is the trail a man can follow, but there will also always be a scent trail—the dog's trail. Scenting dogs trust only their nose in following a trail, and are usually indifferent to the visible signs.

Many animals make scent-trails with secretions that are exuded from their feet. Man-made trails are more complex for scenters to follow. Two decades ago it was thought a dog followed a single odor given off by a man. Modern experiments prove that the trail of a man is a mass of mixed scents—a bank of odors. There's the smell of boot leather, of warm feet, of crushed grass,

Paul's Photos, Chicago

LORD EFFINGHAM'S FAMOUS RETRIEVER "MING"

of mashed leaves, etc. From this medley, a tracker-dog learns to distinguish the telling odor of a particular man.

However, lost dogs that find their way home from long distances do not use their scenting ability, as is often believed. They follow a remarkable homing instinct, which seems almost as strong in the dog as in the pigeon. Perhaps the most dramatic account of a homing dog is the story of Moffino, a dog of Milan, who, separated from his master when an ice floe divided in Russia, found his way back to Italy. This man and dog had gone north with Napoleon on his unhappy expedition to Russia.

Guarding dogs, such as the loyal collie, the busy terriers, and the German shepherd have a highly developed sense of hearing. Often for no apparent reason a sleeping collie will rise, shift its standing, or prick its ears to catch some distant sound, and then raise a cry of warning.

Both hunting and guarding dogs, as well as sporting dogs such

Courtesy Dr. R. W. Johnson, Evanston, Illinois

THE FRIENDLY LITTLE COCKER
SPANIEL

as the pointers and retrievers, are most popular in the country. In the city, where smaller dogs are more desirable, the terriers and toy breeds are favorites.

Cocker spaniels roll their soft dark eyes in more American homes than does any other breed, recently replacing as most popular the beloved Boston terrier, who is known as the "American Gentleman." The whimsical little scottie is an ever increasing favorite.

The exquisite miniatures of dogdom, the toy breeds, have a constant popularity. The *chihuahua* has been known to weigh less than two pounds. The serious Pekingese, sleeve dog of the old Orient, has a romantic history. Sacred for centuries in China, the "peke" was introduced to the Western World after the British looted the palace at Peking in 1860. Four of the little dogs were found behind some draperies in the apartment of an aunt of the Chinese emperor. In other rooms of the vast palace, dozens of dead Pekingese were found—killed by the retreating Chinese to keep the sacred breed from falling into the hand of western men.

DOGS OF THE SEA AND THOSE OF THE ARCTIC

Although he has no standing in official dogdom, the dog of the tramp ships of the sea lanes is an amusing, hardy pet. The roll of the sea does not affect him; he appears to enjoy rough water; and he is the first of the ship's company to sniff a landfall. A true ship's dog (born of a sea-going mother) has a vigorous contempt for "landlubber" dogs.

In the desolate North near the Arctic Circle, where men must make their living by hunting the polar bear, the seal, and walrus, and by capturing the whale, the sledge dog is supremely important. An Eskimo with a good-working dog team can support his family; and an Eskimo without sledge dogs is in a desperate situation. The most famous breeds are the Samoyed, the dog of the great arctic and antarctic expeditions; the Siberian husky, the speedy, enduring, keen-minded trail dog of Siberian snow lands, many times winner of the grueling annual race from Nome to Candle and return; the Alaskan malamute, remarkable for its hauling records, its beauty, and for its work on the Byrd Antarctic Expeditions; and the Eskimo dog, claimed to be the best-footed, toughest, and strongest for his size, of all dog breeds.

Eater of frozen fish, or frozen meat, the sledge dog is a perfect example of adaptation to climate, and the conditions of food supply. He gulps his frozen meals, and the hard, cold chunks can be felt in his stomach, for his dinner must melt before he can digest it. The sledge dog is light enough to pull his burden over thin ice, yet sturdy enough for long hauls. He's affectionate, loyal, and enthusiastic. He appears wildly happy when his driver cries "Huk! Huk!" the signal to mush, and off he goes down the long hunting-trail.

Courtesy Canadian National Railways

IN THE QUAINT OLD GASPE COUNTRY OF QUEBEC
Dogs are extensively used for all sorts of work. This sled-dog is hauling vegetables to the local market at Newport, Gaspe Peninsula.

The keen-eyed German shepherd appears to have great capacity for education and a surprising ability to apply training to daily problems. The German shepherd seems to use judgment. Loyalty, poise, courage, and steady calm are the qualities of a true German shepherd. It has a keen nose, and has been developed to a peak of physical perfection. This powerful breed, an alert protector and a faithful companion, is a punishing fighter when there is need. As a worker-dog, the German shepherd is used by police departments and by custom offices, but its most spectacular accomplishment is its new service to man—leader of the blind.

THE SEEING EYE

In 1928, a blind young American, Morris S. Frank, learned from a magazine article about the work Mrs. Harrison Eustis and the geneticist, Elliott S. Humphrey, were accomplishing in breeding and training German shepherd dogs at Fortunate Fields, Switzerland. The dogs were used by the Swiss and Italian police as patrol and tracking agents.

Courtesy Seeing Eye Training School

"COME ALONG, MASTER, LET'S GET OUT OF THIS TRAFFIC"

Mr. Frank was fascinated by the thought of having a dog to guide him. He wrote to Mrs. Eustis. She replied with an invitation to Fortunate Fields. Soon Mr. Frank was training with the dog, Buddy, who later became internationally famous for his amazing ability as a guide for the blind. Mr. Frank returned to the United States to test Buddy in New York traffic. The experiment was an immediate success. Mr. Morris soon influenced Mrs. Eustis to move her dog-training station to the United States, and to concentrate on developing guide-dogs for blind persons; so the Seeing Eye, Incorporated, was initiated. Here dogs are

Courtesy Seeing Eye Training School

LEADING HIS MASTER THROUGH TRAFFIC

taught to lead blind men—and blind men are taught to follow the trained dogs. Stories of the feats of these dogs are most romantic and at times sound fantastic, but the Seeing Eye school is successful because dogs are not merely turned over to the blind, but both dog and man are carefully trained.

Men and women who enroll at the Seeing Eye school are first given a mental housecleaning by experts in the psychology of blindness. They learn that a guide-dog can lead them away from loneliness and discouragement; and that their new freedom of movement will enable them to become self-supporting.

Students begin by finding their way alone in familiar surroundings. Then each blind person is given a dog already rigorously trained by able instructors. The harness of the dog is equipped with a semi-rigid U-shaped handle that is sensitive to the slightest touch. Assisted by an instructor, the student and his dog begin daily training in Morristown streets. Soon the student and his dog train alone. At the end of the training month the blind "student" and his dog are marked on many points, which

Courtesy Seeing Eye Training School

EXPERTS TRAINING "SEEING EYE" DOGS IN PERFORMANCE
OF THEIR WORK

include ability to pass safely through heavy traffic, and a faculty for meeting many home and office situations, such as the dog's picking up articles that are dropped.

In guiding, Seeing Eye dogs do not memorize their masters' routes, although they become familiar with certain routes by repetition. The blind must know their own route, because the dog's chief purpose is to warn when a route is impassable. Dogs guide their masters away from obstacles and overhead obstructions, and pause at steps or elevations for the verbal signal, "forward," which is accompanied by a forward motion of the hand on the harness. The owner praises his dog when difficult guiding work is accomplished, and this commendation delights the dog. Seeing Eye guide-dogs are perhaps the happiest dogs in the world. They become extremely fond of their masters, and they are conscious of doing useful work.

Almost all the Seeing Eye dogs are German shepherds, because this breed can learn both to obey and to disobey. A successful guide-dog must know when to disregard a command that is unsafe. German shepherd guide-dogs have saved blind masters from innumerable dangers by simply refusing to move when confronted with a situation that holds peril. This *thinking* refusal is the highest type of dog service to man.

The Seeing Eye does not breed dogs, but buys them. It uses about sixty per cent females, but does not regard them as markedly better than male dogs. Dogs must be no younger than fourteen months nor older than two years when they begin training. The future guide-dogs are first trained to be obedient. When they answer commands perfectly, they are given a harness and are taught to meet guiding problems with an instructor. In the final stage of training, the dog is given problems to solve without help.

Within ten years after the Seeing Eye School was organized, more than three hundred guide-dogs were in use in the United States. Mrs. Eustis believes ten thousand are needed. The dogs have a useful span of about ten years; then blind owners must return to the school to be trained with a new dog. Guide-dogs are loved and guarded by their owners. Many blind graduates write the Seeing Eye that they fear an accident to their dogs, because they don't want to *go blind again*. In 1936 Mrs. Eustis received the National Institute of Social Sciences' gold medal "for distinguished services."

THE PROWLING CAT

The cat is man's second most popular pet. It has little of the unselfish devotion of the dog, but rather an amusing—almost human—characteristic of doing unto others as they do unto it! The cat rarely remembers yesterday's benefits. However, this pet is companionable and friendly. Cats have a high degree of dignity and an almost reasoning intelligence. They appear to consider their actions, rarely making a snap judgment about anything, including their acceptance of new human friends. A cat will be courteous, but cool, until an acquaintance is tested.

Paul's Photos, Chicago

BRIGHTEYES HERSELF IN ALL HER
FELINE GLORY

The cat's eyes are contractile; the pupils can expand to gather in even the faintest light. This characteristic has given the cat its reputation of being able to see in the dark. It has a powerful, rough tongue which assists it in chewing and also permits the cat to lap liquids readily; it is the grooming tool the cat uses for many hours each day. Cats are called stealthy because they move silently. Their paws are padded, like cushions. This quietness, true of all pad-footed animals, is necessary for every creature that must pounce on its prey. Cats have curved claws which are drawn back into the pad when not in use.

Perhaps some of the cat's pride in itself, its conviction that it is man's equal, developed three thousand years ago when it was deified in Egypt. The large Egyptian cats, which were hunting cats as well as gods, lived in the Temple of Bast, the cat-headed goddess. While alive they were worshiped; after death they were embalmed and buried in the temple. Ancient paintings show gold-collared hunting cats sitting proudly beside their masters in flat-bottomed boats on the Nile.

VARIETIES OF PET CATS

Cats commonly kept as pets are divided into two classes: long-haired cats and short-haired cats. Most long-haired cats were Angoras or Persians, which are classified according to color: white, black, chinchilla, smoke, silver, tabby, cream, and tortoise-shell. Varieties of the short-haired cat include: white, black, cream, tortoise-shell, Manx, and Siamese.

Two cat oddities are the Siamese and the Manx breeds. Siamese cats, formerly sacred-temple cats of Siam, have fawn-colored bodies and dark masks. They have long, thin faces, bright, blue eyes, and powerfully built bodies. In manner, they are often more like dogs than cats. The strange Manx, which can no longer be exported from the Isle of Man, is tailless and has raised hind-quarters. It waddles when it walks. Manx cats are now rare even in European homes.

The common domestic cat is the worker cat of the world—the cat that plagues the rats and mice on shipboard or on land. He is short-haired, and his color can be any shade of catdom. His breeding is usually a mystery, but he often competes success-fully in cat shows with Persians of impressive pedigrees. Adversity has given the domestic cat strength, endurance, and a tough con-stitution.

Formal cat shows are growing in popularity throughout the world. This phase of cat development originated in Edinburgh in 1875, when a show was held with five hundred and sixty entries. Later, cat shows became frequent in Europe and in America.

MONKEYS AS PETS

Monkeys are, to some people, the most amusing pets man keeps. They are cunning; they love games; they readily become mimics; and their natural agility encourages them to do endless jumping and swinging stunts. They learn to open doors, boxes, and drawers; they deck themselves with surprising ornaments; and they have a most amusing love of comfort—particularly heat and sunlight. Usually they get along well with other house pets, particularly with dogs.

Macaques of the Old World tropics enjoy splashing and wash-ing themselves. The washing is a game to the lively little monkeys, but it has the agreeable result of keeping them satisfactorily clean. Macaques will even wash scraps of cloth, handkerchiefs, or other soft articles, and then will hang them up to dry.

A carefully selected monkey pet is usually gentle and clean, affectionate and intelligent. But caution must be a watchword in choosing this pet. Very young monkeys are always appealing and

MARMOSETS ARE
VERY INTERESTING
PETS

Courtesy New York Zoological
Society

attractive, and at first may hide insufferable faults which they will certainly develop. If the monkey is to be kept indoors, it is essential to avoid the varieties that cannot be housebroken. Care must be taken that the monkey is healthy. Its tail and body should be free of sores, scratches, and vermin. Usually females have the best dispositions and are cleverer than the male monkeys.

Monkeys eat the same foods that are served to man, with the exception that their meat ration must be very small and eaten raw. In addition, meal worms are necessary; so are spiders, flies, and other insects which they will catch for themselves. Bread soaked in milk, ripe fruits, nuts, and seeds, cooked potatoes and vegetables, raw eggs, and canned fish are typical monkey-menu foods.

The monkey cage is usually six times the height of the animal. Inside, there are a few branches for climbing, and a cozy sleeping basket at the top of the cage, for the monkey inherently dislikes and distrusts the ground level. Cedar litter is on the floor. Care must be taken that the monkey cage permits ventilation and the monkey has plenty of fresh air, for this pet, as well as the dog and the cat, often suffers from the lack of air in most human dwellings, according to pet experts.

Several varieties of monkeys can be found in American homes. The mona monkey, whose brown body and golden-green crown measures about fifteen inches, is clean, gay, affectionate, and fun-loving. The black-headed squirrel monkey is a charming pet from South America, with a body about the size of the common gray squirrel. Since this monkey's tail is not prehensile, it cannot use it for grasping or hanging. The brown capuchin is lovable, keen, and is a natural mimic. It has a prehensile tail and a slender, rusty-brown body.

PETS THAT LIVE IN THE WATER

What goes on beneath the sea, or at the bottom of a still pool? These questions have lured men for centuries, and have created the popular hobby of keeping fish. An aquarium stocked with gay, flashing tropical fish thrills many a fish fancier and enables him to study at leisure the ever changing drama of life under water.

Decorative fish were first kept as aquarium pets by the Chinese and Japanese. Later, in imperial Rome, it became the fashion to keep fish in huge outdoor ponds. Somewhere in the long centuries since that time, a fancier devised a glass bowl container. This was an unfortunate invention. The bowl, which caught and has kept popular fancy, is the worst possible container for pet fish, which need air-filled water. They should live in an aquarium which, like a stream, presents a large surface of water to the air. To keep the fish healthy, a fish owner should grow water plants in the aquarium. The plants produce oxygen, and absorb the carbon dioxide gas given off by the fish. Suitable water plants are eel grass, swamp grass, stonewort, and water milfoil.

A second aquarium necessity is the scavenger, a working water-animal that keeps the glass sides and the water free from excess plant and insect life. Snails are interesting scavengers. Ramshorn, fresh-water welk, and Japanese and wandering mud snails are the most satisfactory varieties. The American salamander and the darting weather fish are curious scavengers kept for the same purpose.

Fish that are kept in a general aquarium must be peaceful varieties. Fighting types are often interesting, but they are too destructive for community life. Decorative fish for home aquariums are usually either goldfish or tropical fish, but there is a growing interest among fanciers in native breeds. Tropical fish include a multitude of small varieties that were brought originally from warm seas. The goldfish is a member of the carp family. This little fish was improved by the Chinese many centuries ago, and developed in many strange varieties. All newly-hatched goldfish are brownish-green. They change to sunlight shades when they are six months old. A few goldfish in each hatch do not change color, but retain the dun of their remote ancestors.

BIRD PETS

Birds are the musicians of nature. Man, the music lover, has held them captive for hundreds of years so that he might listen to their sweet songs. When man learned that parrots, crows, ravens, and certain other birds could be taught to imitate sounds and to whistle tunes, these "talking" birds were confined by man. Bird pets have also been kept for the beauty of their plumage and for their sporting qualities. The brightly colored parrots, the parrakeets, the macaws, and the lovebirds are typical plumage pets. Pigeons are kept for sport as well as for food.

All civilized peoples of antiquity honored the far-seeing, fierce falcon. Indians believed it was a god come to earth. In one Greek myth, the falcon is called the messenger of Apollo. It was trained for the hunt by the Persians and other Oriental peoples. When the great migrations of peoples were started to central Europe the sport of hawking was brought westward.

Falcons became adept at hunting all kinds of birds and small game. Later falcons and hawks learned to hunt with dogs. Other birds have been trained to hunt. In Africa and in Asia the eagle is flown after the wolf. Recently, this great sport of the Middle Ages has been revived in central Europe, and today hawking parties are again being held.

The canary is the most popular cage-bird pet, numerically equaling the total of all other cage birds. It originated on the Islands that gave it its name and first reached Europe in the early decades of the sixteenth century. The canary was then a dun-colored little bird that showed occasional streaks of the glorious sunshine color it was to develop. Selective breeding produced the present yellow color of canaries.

Canaries are either "rollers," or type birds. The former are bred for song; the latter are bred by showmen for size and form. Roller canaries range in coloring from green to white. Their value lies in their ability to perform song "tours." About twenty tours are recognized: the glucke, hollow roll, bell roll, bell tour, bass roll, flute, and water roll being the most common. An average canary can sing six tours.

The roller sings with its mouth nearly closed; this gives it a muted, rolling tone. If the bird opens its mouth to sing, the motion of the beak chops the sound, and it is thus called a chopper. A bird that both rolls and chops is known as a warbler. Canary "mules" are hybrid birds that result from a cross between a canary and a finch, or similar bird. The hybrids are often magnificent birds, but they do not reproduce.

FLEET FEET

The earth's changing crust has long vibrated to the hurrying hoofs of one of man's most valuable servants and best friends, the horse. In the Bad Lands of South Dakota are found remains of an early horse antedating the Ice Age. He was one of the herbivorous animals able to escape the carnivorous beasts because of his speed. But the horse of the Bad Lands has been greatly changed through the ages. For example, the number of toes was reduced gradually, as in escaping from his enemies the horse ran on the tips of his toes. Even today, the horse has continued his changing process. Animal husbandrymen, through scientific breeding, have

Paul's Photos, Chicago

A WELL TRAINED JUMPER IN ACTION
This splendid jumper is coming over in fine form, and appears to have every confidence
in its rider.

reduced the weight of the massive Percheron, the common draft horse, by a thousand pounds.

There are two general types of horses: the northern dun, which includes the pony of Norway, the Celtic pony, and the wild pony of Mongolia; and the southern horse—the Arabian, the barb, and the thoroughbred.

Monument inscriptions show that the horse was introduced into Egypt at the time of the Shepherd Kings (about 2000 B.C.). It was first used only in warfare and sport; later it became an object of luxury; finally the horse became a worker. As such he became so important to man that even today we use the term horse-power to measure the capacity to do work.

The domesticated horse developed many breeds and varieties. In the twentieth century there are heavy draft horses; the horse of agriculture, of delivery vans, and the circus rings; another variety includes racers and riding horses; still others, carriage horses, sporting horses, mustangs, and the many kinds of ponies.

Our present horses are not native to America, although fossils indicate that the small ancestor of the horse lived here in past ages. American horses, particularly those of the southwestern plains, the Texas horse and the mustang, sprang from a few horses the explorers Cortés and De Soto abandoned near what is now Texas. Their multiplication on the western plains was rapid. Their effect on the history of our country was tremendous. The poor, inferior, plains Indians soon discovered their usefulness and by the time the American pioneer reached this region, the Sioux, Comanche, and Ute, then on their fast-stepping ponies, became the fiercest and hardest-to-subdue Indians that any pioneer ever faced.

There is one true American breed, the Morgan horse, which originated from the great stallion, Justin Morgan, foaled at Springfield, Massachusetts, in 1793. The Morgan strain is vigorous. There are thousands of these beautiful, untiring chestnut horses in American stables.

Another popular horse in the United States is the English hackney, imported largely since 1890, and used to develop the American trotter. The hackney is not a breed, but a type. It is native to the eastern counties of England and has been bred for carriage service. American trotter fans are enthusiastic about the smooth rhythm of its movement, and the symmetry of its proportions.

Arabian horses are spirited; barb horses are fleet; thoroughbreds are courageous and beautiful; but none of these breeds has the widespread appeal that in the late nineteenth century belonged to the giant horses of the world, the big draft breeds. These slow, splendid, intelligent creatures have been working for man since he domesticated them to replace that stupid beast of burden, the ox. Modern draft horses descended from huge medieval war horses, which went into battle carrying from three to four hundred pounds of armor. A few generations later the draft horse drew the great coaches of France and England down the highways of the kings. Later the draft horse was a common sight in America, pulling a shining plow across a limitless prairie, or busy with world commerce, drawing vans or heavily loaded trucks.

THE MILK CENTURY

We are in the midst of the golden era of the dairy cow. Decades of selective breeding have improved this animal by bringing about early maturity, lengthening of the milking period (cows may now be milked almost eleven months of the year), increasing the quantity and richness of the milk, and through general economy of production. A modern cow produces as much butter as did three or four average cows of the middle of the nineteenth century. Cows today are better fed, better housed, healthier, and larger than their ancestors.

It is possible to compare actual primitive and modern cows. At Chillingham Park, Northumberland, England, there is preserved a herd of the so-called wild cattle of Great Britain. These Chillingham cattle are medium-size, compact in body, and dingy white in color. They have black-tipped horns. These strange cattle are timid and feed at night. The cows attempt to conceal the calves. Because this breed does not mingle with other cattle, and kills any calf that shows deviations of color, its original characteristics have been maintained.

Paul's Photos, Chicago

WORLD'S CHAMPION JERSEY COW
"Stonehurst's Patrician's Lilly," Jersey cow owned by J. S. Lockwood,
Sinnington, Yorkshire, England.

Three hundred breeds of cattle are known today, but the bulk of the milk and beef cattle of the world belong to about a score of dominant breeds. Those most popular in the dairy industry of England and the United States are: Ayrshire, Holstein-Friesian, Guernsey, Jersey, Red Poll, Franch Canadian, Dutch Belte, Brown Swiss, and Shorthorns. Most of these were originally developed in England. The Jersey and Guernsey are famous for the richness of their milk. The Jersey, the smallest of the better dairy breeds, originated from the little Barbary cow of Morocco.

In England and the United States the leading beef breeds are: Shorthorn, Hereford, Galloway, Devon, Polled Durham, and Aberdeen-Angus. All these breeds, except the Polled Durham, originated in England. This breed was originated in the United States by the selection of "sports" which occurred in the shorthorn breed. In size, color, and form they resemble shorthorn beeves, but they are without horns.

THERE'LL BE QUITE A FEW NICE CUTS FROM THIS FINE SHORTHORN BULL

Paul's Photos, Chicago

SECRETARY OF THE DEPARTMENT OF AGRICULTURE COMPLIMENTS THE
OWNER OF THIS ABERDEEN-ANGUS STEER

Paul's Photos, Chicago

HEREFORD CATTLE AT THE GLENDALE STOCK FARM NEAR
ASPEN, COLORADO

The Texas steer, so common in the American Southwest as to seem to be almost native there, was produced from Spanish stock imported in colonial times. However, this type is disappearing because of the introduction of more valuable breeds. Beef breeds have been bred to produce ideal meat cuts. The perfect beef animal is rectangular in outline, low, broad, deep, smooth, and even. Sharp backs are not satisfactory on the cutting block. Medium-sized beef animals are preferred by packing houses.

Down the centuries men have fought the cattle plague, an acute febrile disease that has repeatedly threatened the cattle of the eastern hemisphere. It has been recognized for a thousand years. The plague destroyed the herds of the fierce tribes that invaded the Roman empire during the fourth and fifth centuries, and in 810 A.D. it traveled with the armies of Charlemagne into France. It made a violent appearance in England in 1714. The disease is caused by an ultramicroscopic organism. Fortunately, the plague has never invaded the Western Hemisphere, or Australia.

Courtesy Breeder Publications, Chicago

PRIZE BOAR "RINGMASTER THE FIRST" OWNED BY LAFE PUGSLEY
OF DALEVILLE, INDIANA

THE PIG AND HOG

When the first navigators went to the remote islands of the South Seas, they found the natives keeping domesticated swine. The same animal is also native to Asia and Europe. As a species, it is as ancient as the horse. Although the Jews and the Mohammedans, who form a large part of the world's population, are forbidden the use of pork as food, this meat is the leading flesh food of the world. The skin of the swine is made into leather, its bristles into brushes.

Great Britain originally had two breeds of pigs, the old English pig, and a breed found in Scotland. Our modern breeds have been developed by crossing the native English with either Chinese or Neapolitan pigs. The white breeds, with fine bones, thin skin, short legs, and a tendency to fatten at an early age, get their qualities from the Chinese hog; black breeds, such as the Essex, come from Neapolitan stock.

Popular breeds are: Yorkshire, Chester White, Berkshire, Poland-China, Duroc-Jersey, Cheshire, Hampshire, and Tamworth. The Hampshire and the Tamworth have been produced widely as bacon hogs. The Chester Whites were originated in Chester County, Pennsylvania. Pigs of this breed are large, and some have reached a weight of thirteen hundred pounds. Poland-Chinas were originated in Ohio. The Hampshire is also native to America. In the American corn belt, the great pork-producing area of the Middle West extending along the Mississippi River Valley, the Poland-China is the most popular pig.

Massive five-hundred-pound hogs are no longer favored. The over-fatted type has been replaced by a smaller, leaner hog. Packers ask for a two-hundred and fifty-pound weight. Chicago is the great hog-slaughtering and packing center of the world.

THE ANIMAL THAT CLOTHES MAN—THE SHEEP

Wherever there is pasture land sheep thrive. Down the ages the great, slow-moving flocks have been one of man's greatest sources of natural wealth. Sheep were the most valuable animals of the eras when man was a herder; today they are still important. Their origin is unknown, but they are commonly thought to have descended from the mouflon or the argali.

No domesticated sheep were found in America by the early explorers. The wild Rocky Mountain sheep remain wild. Man has been unable either to domesticate them, or to cross them with domestic sheep. Because it lives in widely different climates, from sea-level to mountain peak all over the world, and because of man's selective breeding, the sheep has developed many variations.

The Leicester sheep of Great Britain was the first breed improved by scientific selection. It is historically important because the Leicester strain was later used to develop all the other long-haired breeds. Most popular among modern breeds of sheep are: Shropshire, Southdown, Cheviot, Lincoln, Rambouillet, and Cotswold.

The finest wool is gathered from the fleece of the Spanish Merino, a native type that antedates the Christian era. Until the

Paul's Photos, Chicago
MONTANA SHEEP MOVING ACROSS SNOW-CLAD
MOUNTAINS TO NEW PASTURES

nineteenth century this valuable sheep was the private property of the kings and nobles of Spain. Iceland sheep and Russian sheep are strange looking animals that frequently grow five horns. One Russian sheep, the Astrakhan, grows its wool in spiral curls and produces a very beautiful pelt sold in the fashionable shops of the world.

THE COCK AND HEN

"Everywhere in the world the cock crows at sunup." This old saying is almost true, because the domesticated chicken has followed man's wanderings as closely as the dog. Its origin is unknown, but the written record of the chicken is old, indeed. An ancient Chinese encyclopedia said: "Fowls are creatures of the west." It seems that they were brought to China about 1400 B.C., probably from the Indian region. Roman invaders, who believed the rooster was sacred to Mars, the god of war, took the chicken to the British Isles.

Although poultry keeping is one of man's oldest pursuits, it has become a new science. Only within the present generation has there been an attempt made to classify chickens, and professional chicken raising is less than a century old. As a food producer the hen is now considered second only to the dairy cow. The leading chicken varieties are: Plymouth Rock, Wyandottes, Orpingtons, Rhode Island Reds, Black Minorcas, Cochins, Leghorns, Bantams, and the Light Brahma.

Cock fighting was formerly a popular sport, but it is now prohibited by law in most countries because of its cruelty. Special breeds of cocks, called game fowls, were used. These birds were so pugnacious and determined that the fights usually continued until one of the battlers was dead.

The long-tailed Japanese cock is an amazing show fowl. This rare breed grows a tail from nine to eighteen feet long. Owners keep the Japanese variety tethered on a high perch so that his tail will not be spoiled. The tail is tied up in a ball when the cock exercises.

Courtesy Chicago Park District

DESIGNER'S NOTE

This volume of The University of Knowledge series is set in twelve point Linotype Garamond. The drawings of animal tracks at the head of each chapter are those of North American fur bearers, such as the Badger, Skunk, Raccoon, Opossum, Mink, Weasel, and other animals.

The design and treatment of illustrations in this book were selected under the expert advice of the authors, which aids materially in presenting a most interesting story to the readers.

OTTO M. FORKERT
Directory of Design and Typography